For Freedom: Theirs and Ours

For Freedom: Theirs and Ours

An anthology of Russian writing

edited by R. G. Davis-Poynter

With an introductory essay by
Michael Foot

STEIN AND DAY/*Publishers*/New York

First published in the United States of America in 1969
by Stein and Day/*Publishers*
Copyright © MacGibbon & Kee Limited 1968
Library of Congress Catalog Card No. 69-17939
All rights reserved

Printed in the United States of America
Stein and Day/*Publishers*/7 East 48 Street, New York, N. Y. 10017

A Note by the American Publisher

THE publication of this book demonstrates the meaning of freedom in more than one way.

Many of the Russian authors included in this anthology are still living and cannot have their work published in their homeland or in their mother tongue. The identity of many, though they are outstanding writers of our time, must be concealed or they will be punished again by their government for speaking their thoughts on freedom.

Their government is the form of Marxist dictatorship that has come to be known as Soviet Communism. For more than half a century the Leninist regime has repeatedly exterminated its leadership and, more pointedly, has deprived its writers and its intellectuals of personal freedom, freedom to write, freedom to say what they mean if they do not speak in accord with the proscriptions of their government. So much is incontrovertible fact.

Though we in the West have been witness to fifty years of repression of intellectuals by changing Soviet regimes, the British editor of this book, Mr. Reginald Davis-Poynter, is still buoyed by the hope that Soviet society's "ultimate goal is freedom."

Mr. Michael Foot, who writes the introduction to this book, is a Member of Parliament and one of England's outstanding radicals. He, too, angered by the Soviet repression of freedom in Czechoslovakia, hopes "that individual Communist states could map out their own paths to democracy." To hold such hope not only after Prague, but after half a century that has included Soviet class and race genocide, the coalition with the Nazis against Britain and the United States and their allies, the rape of Poland, the conquest—in the name of Marxist ideology

—of one-third of the world, and the imprisonment and persecution over decades of some of the best and most talented minds, simply underlines the very human discrepancy between the facts of sorry life and ideological addiction. It is the writers and the intellectuals on the other side of the iron curtain who understand the meaning of freedom better because they have had to live so long with the realities of its repression.

The chief political fact and tragedy is that in the face of contrary evidence people continue to believe what they want to believe. That is why it is singularly appropriate to include as instructive example Mr. Foot's and Mr. Davis-Poynter's hopes that Soviet barbarism will *somehow* cease after fifty years of expansion, half a century without the access to alternatives that is at the core of democracy.

This book after all, is *For Freedom: Theirs and Ours*.

Contents

Editor's Note

This book highlights the dilemma of the writer in relation to a State that should be 'ideal', though contributors such as Tolstoy were spared that dilemma. Others, such as Pasternak, Babel, I'lf and Petrov, Akhmatova and Ehrenburg, although on the whole committed to the revolution and the Soviet State, variously suffered through exile, imprisonment, censorship or terror. Others still, whose work appears anonymously, like the eighty-eight signatories of the August 23 letter to the writers of Czechoslovakia from 'The Writers of Moscow', are still living and working for a society whose ultimate goal is freedom – not only freedom from want, but freedom of expression.

There is only one freedom, and it is not a monopoly either of the 'free' (Western) world, or of 'democratic republics'; it knows no frontiers.

Introduction

A CRIME against freedom; a crime against Socialism; a crime against history; a crime of Vietnamese proportions. No one can find words adequate to measure the sense of outrage and tragedy which swept across the world at the news from Czechoslovakia in August 1968. And one reason was that earlier events in that country had offered a new hope for the whole continent: the hope that all Europe might at last escape from the rigid clamp of the cold war, that individual Communist states could map out their own paths to democracy, that there could be a new birth of freedom, East and West.

Indeed, the adventurous spirit of 1968 in Prague, Paris and elsewhere gave the promise of a new release for Marxism itself and that it could become once again what it should never have ceased to be: a great lever of liberation, a weapon against every form of tyranny, the derisive opponent of censorship and all such offences against the human spirit.

When Karl Marx discovered that his *Rheinische Zeitung* was to be 'put under a policeman's nose to sniff', he unloosed one of his first and most brilliant invectives. Rarely have the claims of the writer been better stated:

'My property is *form*, it is my spiritual individuality. *The style is the man.* And yet! The law allows me to write, but on the condition that I write in a style other than my own; I have the right to show the face of my spirit, but I must first set it in *the prescribed expression.* What man of honour would not blush at such presumption and prefer to hide his head under his toga? At least the toga suggests the head of Jupiter. The prescribed expression only means putting a good face on a bad situation. You admire the delightful variety, the inexhaustible wealth of

9

nature. You do not demand that a rose should have the same scent as a violet, but the richest of all, the spirit, is to be allowed to exist in *only one* form. I am a humorist, but the law orders me to write seriously. I am bold, but the law orders my style to be modest. Gray and still more gray, that is the only authorized colour of freedom. Every dewdrop in which the sun is reflected glitters with an inexhaustible display of colours, but the sun of the spirit may break into ever so many different individuals and objects, yet it is permitted to produce only one colour, the *official colour*. The essential form of the spirit is *gaiety, light*, and you make *shadows* its only proper manifestation; it must be dressed only in black, and yet there are no black flowers. The essence of the spirit is always *truth itself*, and what do you make its essence? *Modesty*. Only the knave is modest, says Goethe; and you want to make such a knave out of the spirit? Or should the modesty be that modesty of genius of which Schiller speaks, then first transform all your citizens and above all your censors into geniuses.'

But, alas, no such light-hearted tone is apposite at the moment. We might turn better to Alexander Herzen, Marx's old rival, who maybe understood the real meaning of tyranny more closely: 'The terrible consequences of human speech in Russia necessarily give it added power. The voice of a free man is welcomed with sympathy and reverence, because with us to lift it up one absolutely must have something to say. One does not so lightly decide to publish one's thoughts when at the end of every page one sees looming a gendarme, a troika, a Kibika, and, in prospect, Tobolsk or Irkutsk.'

Herzen would surely have understood the present mood of his country: 'Scarcely have we opened our mouth, scarcely have we spelt out two or three words of our desires and hopes, when already they try to silence us, already they try to slam the coffin shut on free speech in its cradle! It is impossible. A time comes when thought reaches maturity and can no longer let itself be garrotted by the bonds of censorship, nor by considerations of prudence.'

Herzen also understood the mood in neighbouring lands. In those days it was the Poles who blazed the trail for the countries of Eastern Europe. They came to feel that the war was not between the Russian people and themselves, that there was only one way in which they could fight and which they summarized in a sublime inscription on their revolutionary banner: *For freedom: theirs and ours.*

MICHAEL FOOT

For Freedom: Theirs and Ours

The International

WHEN *The International* is being sung
a purification takes place in me,
and on my lips
              I have a feeling
as if I had kissed the banner . . .

The International
                    jets through me,
when at the Bratsk Station,
                            brother of brothers,
I see side by side
                    Russians,
                            Ukrainians,
Tatars,
        Jews,
              Chuvashes,
                        Buryats.
I believe only in struggle, not in prayers!
I foresee:
          the day of enlightenment, not so far off,
when, like the International Brigade at Madrid,
the peoples of the world
                        will unite.
I foresee a world
                  not impoverished by hostilities,
erecting an eternal cross over squabbles
where the brotherly, united labour of people
give them light
                from a Universal Bratsk Station.

In this Station,
                    delivered from the past,
higher than everything above the earth,
I foresee
            Russia
                    together with a new Spain
                                    and a unified Germany!

In this Station
                in one dining room,
remembering the old days with a smile,
will be an American docker
                        and bearded Cubans,
Israeli peasants
            and Arab fellahin.
Shine out, people!
                Give light!
                    Give light!
                        Give light!
So that mankind will indeed be uplifted!
And the Angara's waves,
                    prophesying this,
sing
    as they rush along
            The International . . .

YEVGENY YEVTUSENKO

Letter to a Non-Commissioned Officer

You ARE surprised that soldiers are taught that it is right to kill people in certain cases and in war, while in the books admitted to be holy by those who so teach, there is nothing like such a permission, but, on the contrary, not only is all murder forbidden but all insulting of others is forbidden also, and we are told not to do to others what we do not wish done to us. And you ask, is not this a fraud? And if it is a fraud, then for whose sake is it done?

Yes, it is a fraud, committed for the sake of those accustomed to live on the sweat and blood of other men, and who have therefore perverted, and still pervert, Christ's teaching, which was given to man for his good, but which has now, in its perverted form, become the chief source of human misery.

The thing has come about in this way:

The government, and all those people of the upper classes that are near the government, and that live by the work of others, need some means of dominating the workers, and this means they find in their control of the army. Defence against foreign enemies is only an excuse. The German government frightens its subjects about the Russians and the French, the French government frightens its people about the Germans, the Russian government frightens its people about the French and the Germans, and that is the way with all governments. But neither the Germans, nor the Russians, nor the French, desire to fight their neighbours and other people; but, living in peace, they dread war more than anything else in the world. The government and the upper governing classes, to excuse their domination of the labourers, behave like a gipsy who whips his horse before he turns a corner and then pretends he cannot hold it in. They provoke their own people and some foreign government, and then pretend that for the well-being or for the defence of their people they must declare war, which again brings profit only to generals, officers, functionaries, merchants, and, in general, to the rich. In reality war is an inevitable result of the existence of armies; and armies are only needed by governments in order to dominate their own working classes.

The thing is a crime, but the worst of it is that the government, in order to have a plausible basis for its domination of the people, has to pretend that it holds the highest religious teaching known to man (i.e. the Christian), and that it brings up its subjects in this teaching. That teaching, however, is in its nature opposed not only to murder, but to all violence, and, therefore, the governments, in order to dominate the people and to be considered Christian, had to pervert Christianity and to hide its true meaning from the people, and thus deprive men of the well-being Christ brought them.

This perversion was accomplished long ago, in the time of that scoundrel the Emperor Constantine, who for doing it was enrolled among the saints. All subsequent governments, especially our Russian government, do their utmost to preserve this perverted understanding, and not to allow the people to see the real meaning of Christianity; because, having seen the real meaning of Christianity, the people would perceive that the governments, with their taxes, soldiers, prisons, gallows, and false priests, are not only not the pillars of Christianity they profess to be, but are its greatest enemies.

In consequence of this perversion those frauds which have surprised you are possible, and all those terrible misfortunes occur from which people suffer.

The people are oppressed, robbed, poor, ignorant, dying of hunger. Why? Because the land is in the hands of the rich; the people are enslaved in mills and in factories, obliged to earn money because taxes are demanded from them, and the price of their labour is diminished while the price of things they need is increased.

How are they to escape? By taking the land from the rich? But if this is done, soldiers will come and will kill the rebels or put them in prison. Take the mills and factories? The same will happen. Organize and support a strike? But it is sure to fail. The rich will hold out longer than the workers, and the armies are always on the side of the capitalists. The people will never extricate themselves from the want in which they are kept, as long as the army is in the hands of the governing classes.

But who compose these armies that keep the people in this state of slavery? Who are these soldiers that will fire at the peasants who take the land, or at the strikers who will not disperse, and at the smugglers who bring in goods without paying taxes, that put in prison and there guard those who refuse to pay taxes? The soldiers are these same peasants who are deprived of land, these same strikers who want better wages, these same taxpayers who want to be rid of these taxes.

And why do these people shoot at their brothers? Because it has been instilled into them that the oath they were obliged to take on entering the service is binding, and that, though it is generally wrong to murder people, it is right to do so at the command of their superiors. That is to say that that fraud is played off upon them which has occurred to you. But here we meet the question: How is it that sensible people – often people who can read, and even educated people – believe in such an evident lie? However little education a man may have, he cannot but know that Christ did not sanction murder, but taught kindness, meekness, forgiveness of injuries, love of one's enemies – and therefore he cannot help seeing that on the basis of Christian teaching he cannot pledge himself in advance to kill all whom he may be ordered to kill.

The question is: How can sensible people believe, as all now serving in the army have believed and still believe, such an evident fraud? The answer is that it is not this one fraud by itself that takes people in, but they have from childhood been deprived of the proper use of their reason by a whole series of frauds, a whole system of frauds, called the Orthodox Faith, which is nothing but the grossest idolatry. In this faith people are taught that God is triple, that besides this triple God there is a Queen of Heaven, and besides this queen there are various saints whose corpses have not decayed, and besides these saints there are ikons of the Gods and of the Queen of Heaven, to which one should offer candles and pray with one's hands; and that the most important and holy thing on earth is the pap, which the parson makes of wine and white bread on Sundays behind a railing; and that after the parson has whispered over it, the wine is no longer wine, and the white bread is not bread, but they are the blood and flesh of one of the triple Gods, etc.

All this is so stupid and senseless that it is quite impossible to understand what it all means. And the very people who teach this faith do not tell you to understand it, but only tell you to believe it; and people trained to do it from childhood can believe any kind of nonsense that is told them. And when men have been so befooled that they believe that God hangs in the corner, or sits in a morsel of pap which the parson gives out in a spoon; that to kiss a board or some relics, and to put candles in front of them, is useful for life here and hereafter – they are called on to enter the military service, where they are humbugged to any extent, being made to swear on the Gospels (in which swearing is prohibited) that they will do just what is forbidden in those Gospels, and then taught that to kill people at the word of those in command is not a sin, but that to refuse to submit to those in command is a sin. So that the fraud played off on soldiers, when it is instilled into them that they may without sin kill people at the wish of those in command, is not an isolated fraud, but is bound up with a whole system of fraud, without which this one fraud would not deceive them.

Only a man who is quite befooled by the false faith called Orthodoxy, palmed off upon him for the true Christian faith, can believe that there is no sin in a Christian entering the army, promising blindly to obey any man who ranks above him in the service, and, at the will of others, learning to kill, and committing that most terrible crime, forbidden by all laws.

A man free from the pseudo-Christian faith called Orthodox will not believe that.

And that is why the so-called Sectarians – i.e. Christians who have repudiated the Orthodox teaching and acknowledge Christ's teaching as explained in the Gospels, and especially in the Sermon on the Mount – are not tricked by this deception, but have frequently refused, and still do refuse, to be soldiers, considering such occupation incompatible with Christianity and preferring to bear all kinds of persecution, as hundreds and thousands of people are doing; in Russia among the Dukhobors and Molokans, in Austria the Nazarenes, and in Sweden, Switzerland, and Germany among members of the Evangelical sects. The government knows this, and is therefore exceedingly anxious that the general Church fraud, without which its power could not be maintained, should be commenced with every child from early infancy, and should be continually maintained in such a way that none may avoid it. The government tolerates anything else, drunkenness and vice (and not only tolerates, but even organizes drunkenness and vice – they help to stupefy people), but by all the means in its power it hinders those who have escaped from its trap from assisting others to escape.

The Russian government perpetrates this fraud with special craft and cruelty. It orders all its subjects to baptize their children during infancy into the false faith called Orthodoxy, and it threatens to punish them if they disobey. And when the children are baptized, i.e. are reckoned as Orthodox, then under threats of criminal penalties they are forbidden to discuss the faith into which, without their wish, they were baptized; and for such discussion of that faith, as well as for renouncing it and passing to another, they are actually punished. So that about all Russians it cannot be said that they believe the Orthodox faith – they do not know whether they believe it or not, but were converted to it during infancy and kept in it by violence, i.e. by the fear of punishment. All Russians were entrapped into Orthodoxy by a cunning fraud, and are kept in it by cruel force. Using the power it wields, the government perpetrates and maintains this fraud and the fraud upholds its power.

And, therefore, the only means to free people from their many miseries lies in freeing them from the false faith instilled in them by government, and in their imbibing the true Christian teaching which is hidden by this false teaching. The true Christian teaching is very simple, clear, and obvious to all, as Christ said. But it is simple and accessible only when man is freed from that falsehood in which we were all educated, and which is passed off upon us as God's truth.

Nothing needful can be poured into a vessel full of what is useless. We must first empty out what is useless. So it is with the acquirement of true Christian teaching. We have first to understand that all the stories telling how God six thousand years ago made the world; how Adam sinned and the human race fell; and how the Son of God, a God born of a virgin, came on earth and redeemed man; and all the fables in the Old Testament and in the Gospels, and all the lives of the saints with their stories of miracles and relics – are nothing but a gross hash of Jewish superstitions and priestly frauds. Only to a man quite free from this deception can the clear and simple teaching of Christ, which needs no explanation, be accessible and comprehensible. That teaching tells us nothing of the beginning, or of the end, of the world, or about God and His purpose, or in general about things which we cannot, and need not, know; but it speaks only of what man must do to save himself, i.e. how best to live the life he has come into, in this world, from birth to death. For this purpose it is only necessary to act to others as we wish them to act to us. In that is all the law and the prophets, as Christ said. And to act in that way we need neither ikons, nor relics, nor church services, nor priests, nor catechisms, nor governments, but on the contrary, we need perfect freedom from all that; for to do to others as we wish them to do to us is only possible when a man is free from the fables which the priests give out as the only truth, and is not bound by promises to act as other people may order. Only such a man will be capable of fulfilling – not his own will nor that of other men – but the will of God.

And the will of God is not that we should fight and oppress the weak, but that we should acknowledge all men to be our brothers and should serve one another.

These are the thoughts your letter has aroused in me. I shall be very glad if they help to clear up the questions you are thinking about.

LEO TOLSTOY

Invocation

Don't be sorry for me! I'll still live –
a good-conduct convict, a happy beggar,
living in the North as a frozen Southerner,
or else a consumptive and wicked Petersburger
in the malarial South, yes, I'll still live.

Don't be sorry for me! I'll still live –
like that lame girl who came out on the church porch,
or that drooping drunkard whose vodka breath could scorch
the tablecloth, or that icon-painter whose torch
scarce lights the Mother of God, yes, I'll still live.

Don't be sorry for me! I'll still live –
like that girl who has learned to read and write
who will be my poetry in the blurred future's sight,
whose fringe like mine will catch the same red light,
who like a fool will know that I'll still live.

Don't be sorry for me! I'll still live –
more merciful than a nurse to a hussar
in the mad pre-slaughter recklessness of war,
and living under my own, my most bright star,
be sure of this, somehow, yes, I'll still live!

Evgenia Ivanovna (Mrs Pickering)

THEY ARRIVED in Zinandali late at night. A strange building loomed up ahead of them through the trees. The car spat into the darkness, then stopped and sank on its back wheels.

While Stratonov was lighting his pipe, Evgenia Ivanovna glanced at her husband. The Englishman was half asleep, his head resting against the back of the seat. His hat had fallen on the side of his head, his lips were drawn tight in a wide thin line. The paroxysm was beginning again. He was clearly far from well.

Stratonov sounded the horn; in a second the sound was lost in the deep silence of the countryside. A great sleep enveloped the Alazan valley that only an earthquake could have disturbed. In this remote spot the word Intourist had no great magic and nobody rushed out to take the travellers' luggage.

'What about getting out and doing something, Katzo?' Stratonov snarled at the driver. 'Otherwise you could lose your job, you know. Go and knock at the door, man. And not to-morrow, please... Nobody's going to run off with your damned Buick.'

The other man exploded at last into the vernacular. It was Stratonov's bloody business to do the foreigners' dirty work, not his. It took a series of threats and a reference to at least three important Caucasian officials to get him to move at all. Finally, he got out, swearing in Georgian, found the nearest door and proceeded to batter on it.

Evgenia Ivanovna was overcome with nausea after the drive over the bumpy mountain roads. She had been almost in tears when they had had to search for a way over the foaming Iara; at the Telav bridge she had got out and walked for a while to get some air and to be by herself.

'I am feeling ill,' she said, as she climbed out of the car . . .
'Please call me when they come for the luggage. And, Mr
Stratonov, would you leave the car door open, please. Some
brands of tobacco upset my husband.'

The cool bitterness of the autumn grass and the shepherds'
bonfires swept across from the mountain slopes. The dense
foliage overhead made a darkness about her like the darkness
before the world began. She heard a rustling behind her and
moved on into the garden, picking her way cautiously along a
gravel path.

'You have an unerring instinct, Mrs Pickering . . .' Stratonov
murmured in French. The unaccustomed language only partly
disguised the voice that to Evgenia Ivanovna was so painfully
familiar. 'One of our most treasured literary monuments is here
in this wilderness – we can visit it tomorrow, if you like. I should
not advise you to inspect it in the dark – for a number of
reasons. Besides, the Zinandali plateau ends just near here in a
precipice and your impressions might be somewhat spoiled . . .'

Stratonov insisted on talking French. He was implying that,
under present circumstances, it was wise to pretend they did not
know one another. He had made this clear before . . . back in
Tiflis, he had seemed to suggest that they should forget that,
some years earlier, they had known one another and he had dealt
her a blow then that had nearly finished her. It was difficult to tell
what lay behind the mask of meticulous politeness. Was it
shame, or pangs of conscience? If it was a sense of guilt – his
torment should have been greater.

It had been Evgenia Ivanovna's first love and it had started one
day about Christmas time in a small, peaceful town in the steppes.
Stratonov had come to stay with his mother – a civil servant – to
recover from a wound. When he had come out of hospital, there
had been a dance in the girls' school. The young lieutenant, his
arm in a sling, had danced with the girls in turn and they had
gazed at this young war-hero in adoration – all except one. It was

conceit that had first drawn him from his exalted position towards the shy, resisting girl in the brown dress and lace pelerine
that was the uniform of the older girls. Near the school there was
an avenue of old acacia trees that was called the Avenue of Loving
Souls. It led across a graveyard of weird beauty out towards the
steppes, blue in the moonlight.

The young people found it amusing that their families had
never met though they lived on opposite sides of the street. Up
until the February revolution the civil servant and the widow of
the local doctor tried to make up for lost time by mutual visits
and good advice. Then the young lieutenant had to return to his
regiment. At Shrovetide, just before he had to return to his regiment there was a party and the young officer recited a poem he
had written himself. Delivered in the sing-song voice that was
fashionable at the time, the poem expressed the desire that a
certain bright-eyed young woman would inspire the writer with
courage to conquer all the enemies of the life that was to start
again. The mothers exchanged glances, considering themselves
already related. And they shrank at the mention of the doomed
'enemies' the tyrants, among whom they numbered the local
Latin teacher, an indefatigable persecutor of lazy pupils and the
local grocer who allowed them credit only until the next old age
pension day. It was decided that they would have the wedding as
soon as, God willing, the war should be definitely lost. But then
there was first a shortage of sugar, and then other shortages and,
in the end, the two old ladies decided to postpone the wedding, as
life itself was to be postponed, until the 'trouble' was over.

In the autumn of the following year the young lieutenant
returned in secret and hid in the haystacks in the field, or in his
future mother-in-law's attic. All that winter, shots rang out in the
night and by the time spring came, many of the local tyrants had
had a hasty burial in the cold earth. Those were the days of that
ephemeral host of Russian chieftains, those commanders of the
universe and other flotsam, who, armed to the teeth, charged

about the steppes with revolvers and swords, on horseback or in whatever transport they could find, shooting at each other as they went and settling in clouds of dust at the side of the road. The town had an influx of stern-looking colonels bent on appeasing an awakened Russia; they were to be seen about the streets, white bashliks over their wasp-waisted Caucasian uniforms. General Denikin himself on his way through, spoke from the church porch, calling the local eagles to be patriotic and the latter, stinking of carbolic acid, their heads shaved, waved and shouted 'hurrah' with all their might. There were charity masked balls for war-orphans, parades and solemn courts-martial. There was gunplay and there was endless gambling, that crazy Russian pursuit of phantoms. Soon the mould began to spread and the great red wave of fire came rolling and crackling down from the north towards the steppe.

One evening, his insignia missing, his epaulettes torn off, the lieutenant came to say good-bye to his future bride. It was hard to recognize the young law student in this shivering smoke-coloured old man. 'Zhenia, my angel, my Ophelia, my sweet cherry-branch; I shall think of you all the time, wherever it is I go – through the desert of ... I don't even know the name of the place,' he snapped his fingers, faltered and burst into tears like a child. Outside there was gun-fire; the rioting garrison had locked itself in the barracks. The day before a red squadron had galloped through the town with great hue and song. Time was running out. Already the first troops of the White Army were being packed into the hold of a foreign ship somewhere by the sea ... Evgenia Ivanovna chose to go with her beloved. At first he resisted the idea violently but he knew that now, as an officer's bride, she was no longer safe at home, either. The mothers blessed them and tried to burden them with the two trunks that should have been their inheritance. They got away in a hired cart, obtained by force which the spirit of evacuation rendered legal. The wedding night took place in the steppe under the sky.

The first snow was whirling in the darkness, their horse stood patiently waiting still in harness, the air was full of the heavy smell of ripe melons from a nearby field. The countryside was alive with silent pursuers hunting down those who had got away and terror multiplied Stratonov's ardour. . . . Zhenia's knees were cold. . . . While her husband carefully hid their bags of oats – for their journey was to be very long – Zhenia gazed at the red glow in the sky behind them, thought of her mother and wondered whether it was worth while being born at all.

Evgenia Ivanovna shivered now as she remembered the years that had followed that wedding night under the stars.

Six months later Stratonov abandoned her, penniless, in Constantinople. After a long period when they had hardly anything to eat, he went out one morning to look for work and did not return. Her first fear was that he had been run down by a tram and, for three days, Zhenia went from one mortuary to another in the strange city, searching for him. She was young and simple and had imagined that death would take them both together when their bodies were tired of happiness. And even then their souls would be together. It was on the fourth sultry day after he had gone, when hunger had almost made her forget her grief, that the real coldness of solitude hit her. She was in the little square, in front of the great cathedral of St Sophia on which she remembered often, when in his cups, her father had dreamt of erecting the Orthodox cross.

She had sat there, suddenly chilled to the bone, and had pressed the palm of her hand to her mouth. In the square, ponderous and swarthy Turks went about their business. Her mother-in-law's brooch and her mother's gold chain had been sold in the first month. Only a chosen few managed to find work washing dishes in the restaurants. There was barely any strength left to fight the temptations of an easy life, and the threshold of destitution, beyond which comes complete insensitivity, was very near. The brightness in her eyes had gone; something of the coarseness of her father's features had begun to appear in her own. There were others like her and together they ran from hunger, this way and that, under the feet of smart, well-fed strangers. Even in her dreams Zhenia longed to be dead in the grave beside her husband. Perhaps, however, the longing was not quite deep enough for it was three years before she reached the limit of her endurance ... This was in Paris, where the wind of exile had carried her after months of wandering from one Balkan capital to another.

Her Russian neighbour in her lodgings had gassed herself the day before – she had been older than Zhenia and uglier and had nothing to sell. For that matter, neither had Zhenia. Russian girls in Paris could not compete with the bored overdressed creatures that sauntered and swung their hips from the Madeleine to the Opera. Apart from the absence of professional skill, it would have taken a few good meals to fill out the hollow cheeks or get rid of the deep shadows under her eyes. So far she had managed to stave off this particular solution to her problems, saying 'I know it will come soon – but oh, God, not today'.

It was her darkest day since she left Russia. Then there had been the same grey funereal drizzle. Zhenia sat under the wet canopy of a café and imagined herself floating down the Seine, bloated, hideous, but at peace. It would be for the best; there was nothing left to regret and there was nobody to try to make her change her mind. She got up from the table to pay and the coin she had ready slipped out of her hand. On her knees, weak with shame, she searched hopelessly among the cigarette ends and puddles on the pavement. The waiter and the customers stared at the holes in the soles of her stockings. She was in despair when a gaunt, odd-looking creature at a nearby table suddenly interfered. The coin had rolled, it seemed, under his hat which had fallen on the ground. It was not until she had paid her bill with it that Zhenia realized that this coin had been worth three times as much as the one she had dropped. In some confusion she dashed after the stranger at least to return the change to him – one thing led to another... M'sieu turned out to be very amiable. He was tactful and understanding and, in due course, he offered Zhenia the task of copying some material for him; some old catalogues from the National Museum in Cairo. The payment was adequate, the paper was supplied by the employer and Zhenia could copy from printed matter without mistakes.

Beyond this, M'sieu had no embarrassing demands to make of her. M'sieu was an Englishman, unfortunately only passing through Paris.

There was enough work to last a month, after which Mr Pickering was to lead an important expedition to Mesopotamia. Zhenia heard this news with a bleak face. Then miraculously it transpired that the Englishman's private secretary had given notice only the day before. That young gentleman had been concentrating apparently on the comparative study of alcoholic beverages but, during the last six months, even the most moderate duties asked of him by the professor had come between him and his devotion to his favourite subject. One might have thought from what the Englishman said that the trip to the East would have to be cancelled and British science would suffer irreparable damage if Zhenia did not step in to fill the vacant position. For Mr Pickering, it seemed, the less experience secretaries had, the better, for, that way, they learned all the quicker to adapt themselves to their employer's way of working. Besides, he needed practice in Russian. He had known it so well in his student days that he could compare the styles of different epics but now his vocabulary was poor.

The decision had to be taken immediately. They were to cross the Mediterranean and arrangements had to be made. Zhenia could say nothing and sat, her head low, her face flushed with confusion.

'Tell me what it is that frightens you, Zhenia: is it the long journey or are you frightened of being sea-sick? Do you think you would hate the discomfort? I know what it is – it's my odd appearance! It might draw too much attention! That must be it.' He was half joking. 'Or perhaps there are sentimental reasons why you prefer not to leave Paris?'

Zhenia was horrified by such a suggestion. 'Oh no, there's nothing like that at all,' she whispered. 'That was a long time ago. I can't really explain it to you.'

'I have no desire to probe into your private affairs any more than I would be likely to go through my employees' luggage when they leave me. I think the journey would do you good. There's too much sorrow in your eyes. You're far too young to be so sad.'

Zhenia had other reasons for hesitating. As far as sea-sickness was concerned, she'd had some experience of sea travel before when she'd spent sleepless nights and days huddled on deck with hundreds of refugees like herself, all shouting and singing, drinking and weeping and cursing the day they were born, to the sound of a guitar. She had not closed her eyelids then for forty-eight hours.

Now she was off to Africa in a cabin of her own – and who knows what adventures Africa might have in store for her? Chasing elephants? The word 'Africa' was on the tip of her tongue for she had been thinking of it all day. She had just received sad news of Stratonov, confirming the rumour she had heard earlier, that he had joined the Foreign Legion, the last desperate refuge of all the dregs of Europe and that he had been killed in a skirmish in Algeria, defending the port of Algiers from rioters. His last thoughts, apparently, had been of his wife.

In her grief, Zhenia did not at the time question the abundance of pathetic detail with which Stratonov embroidered the story of his own death. No, there was nothing left to keep her in Paris – only – here she hesitated – she had no clothes for a long journey, only the clothes she stood up in and these would soon be worn out with the constant washing. If it had been a little later, and she'd had time to pay her debts, perhaps she might have been able to buy what she needed. . . . Then, and it must be admitted it was another miracle, it seemed that one of Mr Pickering's publishers, a partner in a large department store, had gone bankrupt and had paid a part of his royalties on a book of Sumerian inscriptions, in ladies' clothing. It was strange that the clothes were exactly Zhenia's size. It was better, however, not to inquire too closely into such an amazing coincidence, particularly as Zhenia was to receive the clothing in lieu of salary. 'I beg your pardon . . . what inscriptions were they, you say?' she asked out of politeness. But when it was discovered that the absent-minded Mr Pickering had accidentally saddled himself with a number of inexpensive but superfluous suitcases, Zhenia refused tearfully but absolutely to accept them.

. . . The ship was enormous. It had three funnels and its sides were still camouflaged. A child might have drawn the thick spiral of smoke that rose from the main funnel. Hanging over the rail, the passengers seemed absorbed in watching the loading of the cargo, but in fact hundreds of eyes saw Zhenia as she walked up the gangway with the Englishman. Now she was one of them and stood with them in the fresh sea breeze, gazing at the wonderful new world below, shimmering in the sun. As far as the eye could see there were busy people sweeping, scrubbing and painting, ridding the world of all the dirt and dust that had settled on it, so that the beauty could shine through. Farther out there was an ancient fishing boat and even on it there were people, adults and children, scraping the deck, mending the masts, preparing for years of prosperity. Somewhere a band was playing. Flocks of white birds soared in the sky.

Zhenia's thoughts were elsewhere when the dark-skinned tugboat pilot manoeuvred the giant out of the harbour towards the open sea. A smell of fish floated up towards her and her head swam a little when the ship turned broadside to the waves. She wished she could halt the tide of miracles that was overwhelming her. Suddenly there was a deafening rush of steam and surrounded by farewells Zhenia said aloud a prayer of her mother's – that God should have patience and not withdraw from her yet this most merciful of all his whims. The thunder of the wash drowned everything else; soon the birds that skimmed the pearl-grey surface of the water were left behind. Marseilles dwindled in the twilight; the gardens and squares of seaside villas became a ribbon of lights. . . . Though it was time to make the acquaintance of her travelling companions, Zhenia lacked the courage to ask about the other members of the expedition – and indeed she never came to know them at all. Her brain was full of terrifying thoughts as if she was having a nightmare but she feared to wake up might be more terrifying still. Timidly she asked her companion when he was due to return to England. At the beginning of October he was starting his lectures at the University. She dared not ask on what subject for fear of revealing her ignorance and consequently her indifference – to the man with whom she was embarking on this long and uncertain pilgrimage.

'You know I have been to many places on my travels, but I've never been to your country.' Evgenia Ivanovna finally took the plunge. 'Forgive me for asking – but do you work permanently in London or do you travel a great deal? I've been told that London is all smoke and stone and that it has no soul at all – is it really like that?'

It is impossible to say whether Mr Pickering always showed such tolerance as he did on this occasion or whether perhaps he was in a particularly favourable mood at the time. Oh, but he was quite sure Evgenia Ivanovna's impressions of the British capital would be quite different were he the one to show it to her. And he went on to describe different aspects of London, the fountain-head of so much knowledge.

'I should love to see London . . . if it were ever possible.' Zhenia spoke not without dignity but with a sinking heart. 'I remember reading about it in periodicals and my father used to tell me about it.'

'Did he visit England then? Was he talking of his own experiences?'

Zhenia passed her tongue over her dry lips.

'No,' she replied. 'His uncle on his mother's side was a seaman. But that was many years ago; he died before I was born.' Suddenly she remembered her mother saying that the more alluring the trap, the sharper the teeth. Faint with horror she watched the inexorable speed at which the shore disappeared behind them in the night, and then she stammered, 'Forgive me again – where did you say we were going and what exactly are we going for?'

'We are going to Mesopotamia, to study ancient manuscripts ... I'm beginning to sense again a certain anxiety in your voice – have you something against going to Mesopotamia then?'

'No, certainly not, nothing at all ... on the contrary!' And she looked hopefully upwards to where the unblinking eyes of the Englishman seemed to stare down at her from the darkening sky. His answer had reassured her – she knew a little at least about the country they were going to; she knew, for example, that it was irrigated by two rivers, the Tigris and the Euphrates and that, according to the priest who gave her lessons at school, the Garden of Eden had been situated there at some time. All she had to do now was to gather some information that was perhaps something to work on in the meantime.

'I think you would really like to know something more about me,' the Englishman laughed. 'Go on, then, don't be afraid to ask me questions. To tell you the truth, I was inclined to explain your lack of curiosity about my profession, my family and my tastes insofar as I am your employer as simply the result of tact, consideration, education and perhaps bitter experience. It takes a real friend to excuse another so volubly for a lack of curiosity in his person! I'll make it easy for you. You know of course I am an archaeologist. Quite apart from writing vast volumes about what happened yesterday, I also lecture to those who will continue the same pursuit in the future, so that the continuity of our work is not broken. The past can teach the present how to avoid mistakes in the future, though often the same mistakes are repeated again and again ! It seems there is no greater happiness than to make mistakes. And, incidentally, my Chair is not in London University but in the University of Leeds. Your travelling companion has no family, only a mother, a very beautiful woman, and all I have managed to inherit from her is an even temper; in every other way I am like my father. Unfortunately I was too young when I came into this world to choose a parent according to my taste.' In Mr Pickering's eyes there flashed a spark of humour which, in his country, is a great antidote to sorrow and is indeed valued if not higher than a kind heart, then, at any rate, higher than a good brain. 'Tell me, Zhenia, have you ever heard my name before ?'

Evgenia Ivanovna confessed to her shame that she seemed to remember seeing it, but only in the underground, in advertisements of toothpaste. Or perhaps she'd seen it in connection with some sport ?

'Oh, there are endless variations of it,' the Englishman replied good-naturedly. 'There are a number of Pickerings in Yorkshire in all trades and professions. It's getting quite chilly now – don't you feel cold, Miss Jenny ?'

Mortified at her own ignorance Evgenia Ivanovna ignored the question. However, it must be said that only a year before this excellent name had been in all the papers in connection with the sensational finds at Nineveh, that established Nineveh's rivalry with Babylon. . . . The stern and very topical deliberations of the archaeologist, on the decline of morality in Assyria as a symbol of approaching degeneration was linked by the newspapers with his well-known leftist views, with even a tinge, they hinted, of Moscow influences . . . but at the time, Evgenia Ivanovna had been preoccupied with the 'Situations Vacant' columns. Mr

Pickering was quite happy to remedy the omission and report on his findings.

Reassured by his kindliness, Evgenia Ivanovna admitted that when she had been a girl at school, she had adored the excursions to historical places – but, for all their diggings along the soft ground along the river bed, they had found nothing of any value. Evgenia Ivanovna ventured the opinion that archaeology was treasure-hunting without the profit motive. The professor remarked gently that such a sweeping definition was both inaccurate and incomplete and had been out of date for some fifteen hundred years. He went further and briefly sketched the history of archaeology from its limited, platonic beginnings down to the present day when it has become the spade of history. The nocturnal conversation, in fact, concerned something very far removed from archaeology; it masked an attempt at mutual understanding. It seemed that Mr Pickering's companion had, at one time, been fascinated by mythology and, with another person, almost a relative in fact, now dead, had composed an amusing genealogical tree of the Greek gods and goddesses. Suddenly, in her eagerness to impress her employer with her fondness for his special subject, Evgenia recalled her favourite story of the drowning of the Pharaoh and his chariots, who, she recalled, beat the ocean with chains for the impudence of the stupid fish that had swallowed his ring. It was clear from the silence that followed that Evgenia's interpretation of the story had not had the success she had expected. He leant over the rail for a few minutes watching the water; then he put his binoculars back in their case for the sea mist had made them useless.

'No doubt, Zhenia, you have invented a very economical and unusual Mnemonic system to preserve historical facts in such a concentrated form. But I must have tired you with my talk, Zhenia. And it's cold. Everyone else has gone to bed. It's time we were going, too. . . .'

'You think it's time?' Evgenia Ivanovna whispered, terrified, desperately searching for a reason to keep them on deck. 'But why? Why?'

'Well, if you consider it compatible with the status of the secretary of a scientific expedition, I should say the answer is . . . to sleep!' The Englishman allowed himself a wry smile.

'Let us stay here a little while longer. The night is still quite warm. . . .'

Poor Evgenia Ivanovna was again assailed by suspicions. She remembered with horror the day her landlady, out of pity for her pretty lodger, attempted to arrange for her to join a very respectable 'pension' on the outskirts of the town, where the clients did not subject the young ladies to personal scrutiny but made their choice from an album of photographs and then took them away with them with all expenses paid – so that each assignation had the appearance of a social occasion – not so very different from the present excursion to Mesopotamia. Little shivers ran up and down Evgenia's spine – then, when her body relaxed its tension, she descended the staircase with the Englishman – not because she was prepared to follow the kind of life the landlady had planned for her but because she suddenly felt a longing to put her trust in another human being, for one last time. In fact, their cabins turned out to be at opposite ends of the ship. Alone, at last, Evgenia Ivanovna burst into tears from the sudden realization that her troubles were over, that the long downhill journey was a thing of the past.

There is no greater balm to the soul than to listen to the lap of the waves behind the ship's stern and to gaze out to the crooked sails in the distance, gorged with wind and shining like well-fed horses under the fresh breeze as they pull the small fishing-boats across the white combs of the sea. 'Can it really be true, that a chance misadventure has altered the whole course of my life?' Evgenia Ivanova murmured to herself, still not quite convinced of her luck and terrified by the increasing benefits that befell her. Every small thing intoxicated her now like the rum her dead husband had brought home once. He had been half drunk himself and had forced her to take a little, to forget their troubles for a while. Several times on the journey to Alexandria when she had been standing on deck with the Professor, Evgenia Ivanovna had seen, as in a mirage, the figure of Stratonov gazing at them both with a sad, rather than jealous expression in his eyes. 'Ah, Ghoga, Ghoga, life is so beautiful, why did you give up so early?' Evgenia Ivanovna reproached him for his faint-heartedness. But she wasn't reproaching him in order to resurrect him for another period of shared starvation, she was trying to blackmail him by a display of innocent generosity so that he shouldn't get the idea so characteristic of the perfidious dead to return to the position that still belonged to him. She was so weary of poverty and of the necessity to find the least painful way of breaking away into non-existence from this devilish trap.

It would have been possible to reach Mesopotamia by a cheaper and shorter route but the Englishman's heart was set on visiting all his friends in Thebes during his holiday; he secretly considered Egyptology as his main and still unachieved vocation. Sensational news about the regal tomb of the Amarn period excavated near Luxor had been constantly in the Press over the last six months. The archaeologist was tempted to have a look at the unique discovery which had put his own Ninevian findings in the shade, and to congratulate his now famous colleague on his wonderful success. The tomb of Tutankhamen helped Evgenia Ivanovna to penetrate more deeply the sources of the insatiable archaeological gamble. She found herself in the end completely immersed in the past of humanity, and enjoying the attempt to unravel in an adult way the chaotic laws of the rise and fall of civilizations. Everywhere they went on their travels, the Professor explained the sacred histories of the lands they passed. Holding to the widely spread opinion that time is the best healer, he was in fact lecturing Zhenia on immortality, as though the heart could resign itself to sorrow if reason became convinced of its everyday quality. Thus in a series of entertaining stories she passed the University course of Greek History, Early Christianity and the Levantine coast whence they were now heading, having put Egypt behind them.

Pickering's fame as a man of letters and a lecturer was no smaller than that of his prowess as a searcher for treasures and he was uncannily lucky in this as well as in all games of chance. His erudite lecture on the mummified bee from the funereal headdress of Princess Amenerdis had been incorporated in all the textbooks of the West because it taught more of the Egypt of the twenty-fifth dynasty than any long-winded monograph could have done. But perhaps to no other audience did he lecture in the same depth as he did in this solitary seminar, to a shy, brownhaired girl with a long neck, blue eyes and childish eyelashes – and each time Evgenia Ivanovna felt a new excitement as the great realms of the East were born and crumbled down in front of her. Centuries were whipped back to life – they flew past as on a cinema screen, as if the operator had suddenly gone mad and yet not the merest fleeting trifle was lost. Mr Pickering bestowed upon the woman he loved the words he resuscitated like others do poems or flowers, for the price of an absent-minded smile. . . . Now and then he would explain quite plausibly to his companion that he had abandoned the Mesopotamian expedition in order to allow a certain amount of independence to one of his favourite pupils and pretended that it had cost him no small effort to conquer the jealousy he felt for this younger generation.

'At my age one should hurry. The sun is already setting and none of my dreams have been fulfilled, dreams that make my strange life worth while.'

In his attempt to draw the young woman away from the phantoms that pursued her, the Englishman demanded from Evgenia Ivanovna a working routine that was often exhausting. She had to keep a diary documented with photographs and drawings of architectural monuments, the reproductions of which

were sold everywhere alongside tobacco and soft drinks. The
Syrian sky blazed, the local dress and dark glasses gave no
protection. . . . And almost every night Evgenia Ivanovna
dreamt of a tiny, toy-like garden in the north, with hollyhocks,
where her mother was busy planting tomatoes in the beds and
her daughter, just returned from abroad, was rushing to kiss her
before she would be buried in the earth – and at the gate was the
still figure of a man who was fast becoming a stranger, sometimes crying, sometimes drunk, sometimes wearing his arm in a
sling, always different and disturbing and tormenting, gazing
fixedly at the curl on Evgenia Ivanovna's neck, which he had
loved to kiss when he was alive.

From Jaffa long autocars of blue and silver carried away the
travellers, all three of them to the north, along the ancient
caravan routes. Lulled by the purring noise of the engine,
Evgenia Ivanovna sat by the window, her cheek resting against
the teasing silk of the curtain. Past her flashed chalk white ruins,
shepherds driving their sheep, water carriers and fellahin on their
donkeys – from time to time Professor Pickering would point
out a ruined crusader's castle, or a wool caravan in the distance,
or a Moslem graveyard with helmets on the funereal posts, or a
large rough water-wheel on desolate half cultivated peasant's
land – Evgenia saw it all in a kind of slumber beyond the
swirling sandy wind that beat against the carriage windows and
always her vision included somewhere the silhouette of Stratonov.

Through the ash-grey film of sand she saw the famous towns:
'torches that glowed in the history of the East' as Professor
Pickering described them – Damascus where they heard the
classical cry of the muezzin calling the faithful to prayer, and
Palmira, unique and weathered and treeless.

There they picked up an Arab guide from the local museum;
he looked like a Patriarch in his round cap and picturesque cloak
with which he sported ancient and obviously very tight European

shoes. He showed them the ancient necropolis, the aquaducts and holy places where knotted ivy climbed on the surviving pillars, clawing into the leaves of the capital and fighting for life with a solitary ruin. He explained every stone to the travellers till reverence began to wrestle with sleep. But in the end Evgenia Ivanovna came gradually in this surfeit of information to find respect for the signs of ancient grandeur, of national pride and religious loyalty.

The dry Syrian wind blew gently from the East, producing as it beat against the crannies in the ancient columns, a kind of wild Kurdian requiem.

'The wind is spiteful and restless here!' said Evgenia Ivanovna covering her mouth with her blue muslin scarf. 'A Russian January frost would seem quite benevolent in comparison!'

'You mustn't dislike it, Evgenia,' replied the Englishman, his voice suddenly deafened by a swirl of sand. 'Remember this is the dust of all the ancient Biblical sands and it has seen too much to settle down early and sink into oblivion.'

Mr Pickering spoke Russian with some curious turns of phrase but Evgenia was beginning not to notice. He meditated aloud on this vast land made up of layers of human heart and bone which over the centuries had fought and killed and each time settled down again to mingle with the sand under the burning wind. The sand was tormented and restless, he explained, always looking back to more glorious times when perhaps it had been beautiful, part of a singing wind, perhaps a petal of saffron.

'Do I make it too romantic?' he asked, blushing under Evgenia's stare.

'More,' she whispered, touching his hand and nodding in the direction of a lizard, a contemporary of the ruins, who had come running to listen. 'But don't get so excited. . . .'

'They've gone, all of them, but they remain here, for ever!' And he let a handful of dust from under his feet run loosely between his closed fingers. 'Nothing gets lost . . . in history and biology – it's like in the army; property when it loses its immediate use is stored away in the storeroom. Have pity on it, Jenny, don't complain of it, this dust of former life, for wanting to cling to the living.'

A slave to habit, he finished the lecture with lists of sects, of dynasties, of despots and all the other historical machinations that had transformed minerals, fruits, bones and jewels into the present particles of dust.

Our travellers spent a week in Damascus. Their Arab friend opened up his town to his guests like a holy casket, the town that had been loved by Mahomet, Moab and Saladin. Now and then they would stop to have some coffee with the local Armenian – nowhere in the world was there such good coffee. To get there you had to make your way through secret side streets, permeated with the smell of mutton and almonds. A small fountain splashed in a mosaic pool in the middle of an inner yard and 'Halleluja', so favoured in the post-war years, scraped away on an ancient gramophone, to a background of wailing dogs. The innkeeper would regularly kick a stray dog from under the counter – which ruined his reputation in the eyes of foreigners, particularly the English.

'You know, I don't recognize my teacher today,' Evgenia Ivanovna said one day with a gentle reproach. 'He hasn't said a word all day. Is he tired of the least talented of all his pupils?'

'On the contrary, I've missed you all the time,' he said. 'You spent the day with someone else . . . you've been calling him and sending him away and reproaching him all day long. Is he so very wicked then?'

Evgenia Ivanovna lowered her eyes in embarrassment. 'No,' she replied. 'He is merely wretched and dead . . . I wouldn't like to speak ill of him. . . .'

'Oh, I assure you, I'm not interested in the acquaintances of my employees.'

This unexpected and sudden wave of jealousy prompted

Evgenia at last to tell Mr Pickering the story of her life. She concealed nothing except the dead man's name and the remarkable thing was that from that moment Stratonov ceased visiting his former wife. The last time he imposed his presence was at an oasis near Damascus, where the travellers were invited to the local races.

Nothing remained of that day in Evgenia Ivanovna's memory; neither the dazzling blue sky nor the hoarse exclamations of the racing crowd. She was brought back to reality only by the smell of sweat from the shiny horses' bodies that came to her nostrils and the sudden feel of sand on her teeth, when, to the signal of a depressed looking sheikh a swarm of riders in striped, flowing burnouses threw itself with war-cries on the imaginary enemy. They dashed past, standing in their stirrups and shooting as they galloped, to underline the seriousness of the undertaking.

Tears of gratitude to God came to Evgenia Ivanovna's eyes as she suddenly saw again the sorry years of poverty, humiliation and fear. Everything round her seemed to share with her the ecstasy of being alive, even the cripple with the hairy Adam's apple who pranced in his own weird fashion across the race track, even the proud-beaked falcon perched on a stick behind its owner.

As she stood there, Evgenia Ivanovna found herself thinking of only one thing – what was still to come for her, how many good years would she have left? It was the moment of recovery from all the past, and it was then that Stratonov dropped out of her heart, but so casually that she would have fainted from the pain, were it not for Mr Pickering's helpful hand. The Englishman rubbed her icy fingers under the bench until they thawed in his palm. Evgenia Ivanovna thanked him dumbly with tears in her eyes. . . . That same night her former husband appeared for the last time in her dreams.

It was black as night and Evgenia Ivanovna knew she was surrounded by ravines, but she could see no rocks, not even her own foot on the path – nothing. A nagging anxiety told her that this was no ordinary landscape but the frontier with Russia. Stratonov was hiding somewhere here and instantly she had to know what he was doing in this darkness. She must find out at once, before it was too late. And there he was, she almost stepped on him, lying at her feet on the slope, his head resting in the dry river bed. That meant that it had not been in the African legion, but right here that he was shot attempting illegally to re-enter his country . . . but for some reason Evgenia Ivanovna no longer believed the liar.

Slipping on the pebbles, as she avoided the body, she was stealthily looking for the expected bullet holes on the dead man, but there were none. There was, in fact, something dark on the forehead, but it was too frightening to bend down and feel with her finger to seek confirmation. What if he were to snatch at her. Then she discovered that Stratonov was not really dead at all, quite the opposite. That he lay there watching his wife coldly and mercilessly from under flickering eyelids. Terrified Evgenia woke up and half naked because of the heat, she rushed into the next room and dived under the mosquito net over Professor Pickering's bed, desperate for protection.

The Englishman's dream was coming true but he did not even touch his beloved, feeling, with some justification, that he was only the last link in the chain of her misfortunes. But when the natural paralysis of worship passed, the shyness passed too – and an hour later, Evgenia Ivanovna saw her bare legs in the moonlight and with sinful laughter, stretched out to pick up the sheet that had fallen to the floor. The relationship that sprung up between them on that night progressed with varied success and became legally confirmed about a month after they crossed the Turkish frontier. Thanks to her marriage, Evgenia Ivanovna was able finally to put aside all anxiety as to her daily bread.

The Turkish part of their journey was spent in the wilderness, with excursions undertaken in shaky, tortured vehicles, and their food mainly unbaked pancakes and tiny pieces of goat cheese. The arrival of the couple was always accompanied by a certain surprise. Professor Pickering's journey was not unlike an old fashioned chase in the cinema for although they travelled incognito and zig-zagged across the country, they were continually being recognized and having to move on yet again to escape the scrutiny and cameras of the tourists. During those last weeks before the main adventures of their journey the Pickerings visited three Hittite fortresses and the excavations in Bagaskie where, under the broiling sun they sieved through the former capital of the Hittite Empire in the hope of finding even a solitary inscription. Great eagles circled over the jungles of thorn and blocks of crudely carved basalt. On these could be picked out the faint delineations of ancient gods and their commandments and Evgenia experienced the impatience of the explorer on his first voyage of discovery – it seemed the Englishman had found for life both a companion and a devoted assistant – the ideal combination for such a man. A short while later they moved on to Urfa, the ancient Edessa of whose existence Evgenia Ivanovna had no idea until she actually arrived there.

Professor Pickering was attracted to this place by scientific interests and he had once almost decided to remain a dozen years or so. On his first trip outside the town, he showed his wife his favourite spots where, with the consent of the Turkish government, he planned to discover and investigate the documents which were the key to the history of this ancient citadel, the necropolis of many nations and centuries. According to Professor Pickering, this comparatively narrow arena had been a battleground for thousands of years; it had seen the war between the young European civilization and the ever retreating desert, between East and West, between Hittites and Hurrites, between the Roman eagles and the Persian lions, archbishops and heresiarchs and the powerful Veliarus and the local hermits who plagued him like mosquitoes. The disciple, Thomas, started here on his missionary journey and, three centuries later Efrem Sirin came to the city gates to welcome back the remains of one who had paid fully for a moment's scepticism. In the intervening years Trajan's minions razed the city to the ground; it was later rebuilt by Adrian – it was here that the Prefect Macarin stabbed Caracalla before he was stabbed himself by a Syrian youth. The activities of the Romans in this part of the world ended with the capture of Valerian, whose back the lofty Saporus used to heave himself on to a horse. And in the darkness of time the Mongols, the Crusaders, earthquakes and the plague lay in wait to pounce upon Edessa.

'The old woman has something to remember on a sleepless night. She enjoyed everything and everyone enjoyed her' – the Englishman thus ended his lecture.

'Tomorrow, Jenny, you will finally become Mrs Pickering. I want to believe that one day our marriage will be marked by the local archivist as one of the happier events of local history.'

The whole day passed in visiting monuments, and on their way back from the nemrod ruins they stood by the kilns where, Mr Pickering presumed, the gay fishermen of the goddess, Athervatis, had once frolicked. That evening the couple rested in the cool gardens of the British missionary who had sheltered them. Among tiny jungles with lacquered foliage a stream murmured as though it carried the chirrup of mountain birds and the local crickets. Evgenia Ivanovna hid in the shade, because the sun had been scorching from early morning. Pickering himself, according to his strange habit, bravely sat facing his lady in full sunlight.

'So you don't regret that you have shared this search for happiness with me?' he asked, admiring her tan, the colour of her hair and everything else that had at one time likewise fascinated the dead Stratonov.

'Oh, darling . . .' She almost succeeded in imitating the drawl, with which the Englishwomen she knew expressed their tenderness. 'There is only one thing that worries me. Why do you always sit facing the light, with such fixed uncertainty in your eyes?'

'I want to read what you think about me, Jenny.'

'First of all, I think you are the handsomest man in the world.'

He stopped her with a movement of the hand.

'I am deeply content, Jenny, that you are getting more and more used to my appearance. Ever since I was at school it has caused me the greatest humiliation. There is a line in Tennyson: "Show me the Man hath suffered more than I." When I was a child I thought this was about me. The Divine Creator created me when he was a bit tipsy. Perhaps by bestowing on me the gift of memory and a considerable capacity of penetration which not even my enemies can deny me, he was simply trying to recompense me for his ugly behaviour. . . .' Sadness and humour suited Mr Pickering very well, they added a human dignity to his appearance which for other reasons he lacked. 'It is dangerous to build a family on the quicksands of mere feminine gratitude. That is why I wanted to have this conversation with you before you finally became my wife.'

Then, blushing and stammering, Evgenia Ivanovna agreed that in fact his appearance was a little unusual and under certain angles even slightly comical and could only, under pressure, be called beautiful. 'But, heavens, surely what is beautiful is what you love!' impulsively came from her lips much to Mr Pickering's consolation, who perceived in this admission not only tact or sincerity, but a sort of unawakened intelligence. She added that she believed him to be one of those guardian angels living secretly on earth and ornamenting its sorrows with flowers. And as to the body, why, wasn't it only a mask for angels?

'I will confess to you, my darling teacher, that not all angels fulfil their guardian obligations as thoroughly as you do.'

'Well, personally I would have preferred to remain invisible, so as not to make stammering idiots out of my pupils,' Mr Pickering said jokingly but in a hard, cold voice adding bitterly that he regretted not being able to wear a veil permanently on his face like Mocanna, the rebel against the Arabs.

It is impossible to avoid mentioning any longer the sad phenomenon in the life of this distinguished scientist and gentleman who already at the age of twenty-seven was the editor of the *Annals* and after the deceased Layard was considered the greatest authority on Assyro–Babylonian archaeology. The young listened to him with bated breath when he started on his inspired improvisations – but nevertheless the first few minutes were continually wasted on the stifling of a lightheaded animation among young students. The reason lay in Mr Pickering's appearance, which in detail as well as in general not only poisoned his private life, but was an obstacle to his political activities, provoking in the audience an amusement incompatible with the confidence of electors. Not only, owing to his incredible gauntness, did his right side, against all the laws of nature, find itself somehow on the left one, but the complexion itself was not what it ought to have been. One couldn't deny, either, that under certain lighting Mr Pickering's eyes that lay very close to the bridge of the nose reminded one sadly of a double-barrelled gun. Some other particularities, omitted here only in respect for his learning, like unusually long arms and an unbelievable height, offered such easy material for caricatures and jokes that even his best friends, gentlemen themselves, often indulged in them. The scientist had nothing else to do but, like the sun, dazzle the crowd in order to conceal his spots from it.

Mr Pickering had no family. Only two women visited his home – his cook and his very old, stern, once very beautiful, mother, dressed always in deep mourning. Their rare meetings consisted mainly in patient contemplation of each other, and, in the intervals, of contemplation of the burning logs in the fireplace. Evil tongues, not very discriminating in taste, attributed his scientific successes not without justification to his misfortune, for, unlike archaeologists with families, forced to waste their leisure in fussing with their grandchildren, Professor Pickering had the opportunity of working like a beaver round the clock on the sorting out of his crocks, which he brought in abundance from all over the world. In short, with the years he had delved deeper and deeper into the remains of ancient tombs, where no sunray, no children's laughter, or woman's voice ever penetrated. And he knew so little about himself from this intimate angle, that his long-cherished hope of an heir was paralysed with fear more from lack of habit than from symptoms of age. With his world-wide fame it was the fear of sensational headlines that had driven Mr Pickering with his bitter and unexpected love-affair to an Asia Minor backwater.

After a wound accidentally received during religious demonstrations in Bengal in 1906 the Englishman suffered from acute attacks of neuralgia. Evgenia Ivanovna had become used to looking after him during their travels, marriage did not bring with it many more obligations. Now she called him 'doc', using the American diminutive of his learned rank.... Her absurd fears became dispelled, the gods treated the couple rather favourably. The contents of the Pickerings' luggage lost its separate identity, according to considerations of marital comfort and travelling requirements.

To please his wife, Professor Pickering had organized the return journey via Constantinople. Evgenia Ivanovna could not resist the desire to see again the little square opposite Aja-Sophia, where she had once longed to die. And suddenly on the eve of obtaining the British passport, when the door had opened for her to security, independence of fear, hunger and chance, she fell ill for no understandable reason.

With their progress towards the north the magic details of the journey reflected in her eyes grew more and more dim and the uncontrollable joy of life turned into cold anguish and loneliness.

Evgenia Ivanovna shivered and peered with moist, inflamed eyes into the unattainable northern horizon, concealed in a blue mist. The greatest men in the Turkish medical world found no dire symptoms in the young woman's condition, but the strange ailment washed away her colour and radiance, like a fresco from a wall. The freshness of the skin disappeared with the tan, the eyes darkened with the vanished smile. His wife's spasmodic silence which Mr Pickering was unable to break frightened him even more than her physical disintegration.

Much against his convictions, the Englishman, distraught and terrified that her depression might drive his wife to something wild and final as had happened to so many of the Russian exiles, made certain necessary investigations. In a secret corner of her suitcase he found a gold ring which he hadn't given to her. By this time Professor Pickering knew most of his wife's background and he was not too upset by the inscription inside the ring of a man's diminutive name, not his own – but he knew whose it was. The thing that surprised him was: how did this little piece of gold survive with Evgenia Ivanovna during the days of her Paris misery, when matters of honour and existence were solved with a loaf of bread? In the cloudless sky of hard-won happiness, little clouds of doubt, so familiar in Damascus, reappeared. So the mouldy young Russian gentleman of military rank was again invading the Englishman's castle by the back door?

The next day the Englishman inadvertently caught his wife reading an old newspaper, which immediately disappeared; but Evgenia Ivanovna was unable to conceal from him her tear-stained face. That same night, again, somehow unexpectedly, he discovered at last behind the torn inner lining of a suitcase the mysterious newspaper page, crumpled and almost reduced to dust, which turned out to be the official organ of the Council of Workers, Peasant and Soldier deputies, published in one of the Russian towns in the steppes. The discovery revealed to Mr

Pickering the existence of a second secret plan in his wife's life, luckily not sufficient for political persecution in Europe. Nevertheless even if one was to disregard the justified bewilderment as to the channels by which this provincial Soviet publication, only a year old, had fallen into the hands of a subject of Her Majesty the Queen, another appropriate question posed itself – what could the fugitive find to attract her in the violent diatribes concerning the degenerate West which had been happily decaying ever since Herzen's time, the West which had offered her, if not a too comfortable, anyway a secure refuge? True, it had come to Mr Pickering's ears that some incorrigible wanderers sometimes found security a source of oppression . . . though, even if she suddenly felt nostalgic for the fierce upheavals which held a curious attraction for the Russians of the 1920's – even then, what heart could be affected by the romantics of an epoch for which it had served as a brick or as a target; as to storms, Mr Pickering held a different point of view.

What could be then the attraction for the woman he loved, in that country she had fled in despair, where she no longer knew a living soul. Professor Pickering, who could understand the hieroglyphics of a stone a thousand years old, searched in vain to decipher the sorrowful lines around his wife's childish mouth. The secret lay in the fact that the picture at the bottom of the page represented the Market Square in her native town. And what attracted Evgenia Ivanovna in it was not that, with the help of overtime on Saturdays, it was planned to erect a universal obelisk of the Revolution on it, visible to all the oppressed continents, but something which the Englishman did not know: that in the far corner of the square one could catch a glimpse of her mother's house with the hollyhocks in the garden. They had heard some time earlier through the British Embassy in Moscow, that the old lady had died soon after her daughter's departure. It was only by the elimination of absurd or humiliating hypotheses that the desperate husband came to learn the truth. Beyond the mountains on the horizon was Russia, and despite the physical barrier of the Caucasus and the fund of bitter memories, Evgenia Ivanovna's heart yearned desperately to be there, so desperately that faced by any resistance that quivering bit of flesh would be ready to tear itself away from the body.

In the first direct talk they had together, his wife's dismay confirmed to Mr Pickering the correctness of his diagnosis.

'You mustn't pity me, my dear,' Evgenia Ivanovna replied curtly, but not without affection, while she amusingly puckered her brows, as if pleading with her husband to be patient with her tiresome, Russian sorrow. 'When a storm tears a leaf off a tree – its days are numbered. It can dance for a while in its freedom and fly and even soar to great heights, but in the end it will rot before the others that remained on the tree.'

Her words came out somewhat tritely, as though learnt parrot-wise.

'But this very idea should free you of all attachment,' Professor Pickering remarked without much assurance.

'Of what, of what should it free me?' Evgenia Ivanovna screwed up her eyes in her effort to understand the European mentality.

'Of all obligations to the tree that cast you off, dropped you so ruthlessly . . . it is unnatural to love something that pays you back in hatred.'

'And how long ago did that occur to you, my darling?' his wife smiled with a touch of irony.

'It came from Diderot.'

Evgenia Ivanovna shrugged her shoulders.

'Perhaps that only proves that men of great intelligence find it easier to put down their roots in strange soil than we lesser mortals do.'

A week later, Professor Pickering casually asked his wife if she thought he should accept the invitation of friends in Moscow to go there on his return journey to England. About two years previously, at an International Congress, he had spoken frankly and gratefully of what he had described as Russia's 'bold attempt to introduce some order into the complex social, industrial and moral relationships of the modern world.' About the same time, in a scientific article which had a wide distribution he talked of Moscow's role as 'one of those beacons marking the milestones on the highway of mankind.' And, before leaving for Asia Minor, he had given an interview to a newspaper correspondent in which he compared Russia to the touchpaper keeping alight a declining world. Naturally what he said on these occasions had impressed the Soviet authorities to the point that he was considered one of the short list of distinguished friends of the October Revolution – which explained the ease with which visas were obtained to say nothing of the permission to enter Russia across the Caucasus Mountains, permission not normally granted to foreigners.

His wife put her hands on Professor Pickering's shoulders with silent gratitude – how he loved her rather large, charitable hands!

'You're a magician,' she said. 'And you see everything. I promise you won't be a second late for your lectures. We needn't even break our journeys. We could just have an hour or so between trains, and I could show you that remote village beyond Rostov where I was born. You might even find some mound there that you could excavate . . . So don't be angry, my darling, for I'm made of that same soil, you know.'

In fact Evgenia Ivanovna was making the journey to Russia to ask her country to set her free and to put an end to the torture of homesickness that kept her awake at night. What use was she to her country now, the poor fugitive? Of course it would be better to go in summer to get thoroughly, unforgettably drenched in a steppe storm, or again in the winter to get frozen to the bone in a clearing in the forest, listening to the silence filtered by the gentle fall of snow. And the Russian spring drew her too: she longed to sit at Eastertime by her parents' grave, covered in coloured egg-shell, to whisper with her mother to the heart-breaking yet strangely comforting cry of the rooks. And were this great happiness to come in the autumn, she would spend the allotted hour wandering along the avenue of old acacia trees, listening to the dry crackling leaves underfoot. The path led past her mother's house and so she could find out at the same time if the dog Tresorka was still alive, if the cuckoo-clock was still there and who slept on the trunk behind the screen in the back entrance.

Very unusually, the distinguished guests were allowed to enter Russia by an almost direct route from Karo across the Sakhal-Tutan pass. They hurried to cross the frontier in daylight. Towards evening the weather changed. The clouds overhead rushed towards Turkey. Rain was beginning to ripple the surface of the mountain lake when the travellers transferred to an open car that bore all the signs of a long and heroic life. On the waste ground by the Karsakh barefoot children kicked at a battered tea-pot but all sound was absorbed in the blessed peace of the even-ing, that glowed pink in spite of the ominous weather. Evgenia Ivanovna, who had grown wan in the last hour, kept feeling in her handbag for her new passport as if it protected her against all eventualities. Instead of the expected customs examination and tiresome formalities the local librarian, or perhaps he was a farmer, presented the distinguished foreign lady with a bunch of flowers. She alone stood under an umbrella, everyone stared at her with a significance she could not understand. An orator congratulated the famous *architect* on crossing the threshold of the new world – a printing error of the telegraph service led to friendly gaiety on both sides. All the way to Tiflis the travellers were showered with hospitality, with strange, intriguing drinks, with food and cultural entertainments of all kinds, and with accommodation in the shape of carpets for the night in Akhal-rikli, where a half-successful attempt was made to drink the

Englishman under the table in toasts of universal significance. It all ran very smoothly and there was no constraint or embarrassment on either side, not even when the Pickerings' suitcase with their underclothes in it disappeared and was restored to them later, as it usually is in well-organized countries, with various garments that were not their own. Evgenia Ivanovna drank in every detail on the journey; the naked deserted slopes of the frontier uplands, the magic castle at Khert-pisi and behind Borzhom – the heavy pinewoods, the echoing ravines with streams rushing down to the highway and finally the snowy borders of the main Caucasian ridge in the distance, dissolving in the autumn mist. Twice a blast of damp, cold air blew into her face and then Evgenia Ivanovna began hurriedly to analyse the essence of the changes that had occurred in her, while there was still time before the arrival at the Georgian capital.

In Tiflis they were lucky to arrive in time to hear the popular prima donna still of Petersburg renown who for a generation and a half had held experts spellbound with her beautiful slow soprano. . . . The entertainment began at eight and after a short rest, on their way to the concert, the guests gathered in the reception hall in order to establish their future programme. The local authorities were waiting for them in the manager's study, to welcome the newly-arrived friends of beautiful Georgia. Evgenia Ivanovna, with a deep sigh, entered the elegant room lined with warm curtains, furnished with an elegance and comfort that had once belonged to the late *bourgeoisie*.

'Khakhulia! . . .' the man in the green jacket uttered in a melodious, throaty voice, rising from behind the huge table, stretching out an impressive hand and leaving one to guess the meaning of the word; the others made quacking noises and those who had them stroked their moustaches with an air of dignity.

They started a conversation on the vicissitudes of travel in post-war days and the attention of the Pickerings was drawn to a picture on the wall, painted in a spirit of great sincerity: an amazingly young-looking old man in a black felt cap peered at the guests from an ornate frame: he reclined blissfully under a canopy of bunches of grapes with a horn of wine in his hand, while the sunset glowed behind him as if the heavens too were full of wine.

'What you see here is our sunbathed Kakhetia,' explained the head of the tourist delegation, flattered by the attention of such distinguished people. 'According to learned professors, that is a most favourable spot from the point of view of climate. We have decided, then, to start from the Alazan valley, so that you should not forget Georgian love and friendship' – he ended up and at once the others supported their elder colleague and began, one after the other, to ply Professor Pickering with information, accompanied by explanatory gestures, concerning the healing properties, the untroubled silence and the other attractive qualities of this miraculous corner of the world.

Knowing his wife's plans and intentions the Englishman glanced inquiringly at her; happy and flushed she had already succumbed to the pressure of such warm hospitality. Indeed a trip to Kakhetia would give her much-needed time to put her thoughts into order, a thing which she had not been able to do throughout the journey. The faint inclination of her head was met with unanimous approval. Khakhulia promised to attach to them the best guide in the whole of the Caucasus, with a know-ledge of French, and he shouted into the telephone a disturbingly familiar name, which was drowned in the fireworks of the Georgian tongue. After a short time during which Evgenia Ivanovna tried not to lose consciousness a living Stratonov entered the study behind her back. She recognized him in the mirror by his old brown velvet jacket with a rubber belt and the same worn trousers pushed into dazzlingly shining leggings, that he had worn in the Constantinople days. Mysterious rings and straps on the guide's belt, a map-case hung across his shoulder; heavy double-soled boots gave him the appearance of an experienced mountaineer. So as not to tire them with trifles, the manager did not see fit to introduce the guide to the distinguished tourists and the latter himself hardly glanced at them. . . .

When they came to discuss their itinerary, Evgenia Ivanovna came to her husband's rescue over a sentence he found difficult to put into Russian. At the sound of her voice, Stratonov's eyes flew in her direction and for a second he looked as if someone had hit him – hard. He appeared to choke and seemed on the point of passing out. Evgenia Ivanovna watched in the mirror and saw how, when he recovered his composure, he searched, awkwardly, for somewhere to sit, not to be the only one standing – but the only free chair was occupied by the guests' clothes. So he leant as casually as he could against the door.

'Don't be in such a hurry to die, my friend, give us a smile,' Khakulia called out to him in a strong Georgian accent and in a friendly if proprietary manner. 'Ai . . . ai, an old soldier and look at him, he's like a sick girl! You should try and create a better impression on our good friends here.'

There was nothing insulting in the jocular almost paternal tone, and at once Stratonov's manner was one of a man anxious to please and to inspire confidence; all that was needed now was a sign of approval from Evgenia Ivanovna. She inclined her head slightly in Stratonov's direction. There was nothing to fear from her former husband. There would be no embarrassing familiarity. Humbled and beaten he would never dare to risk upsetting as esteemed a friend of the still shaky Soviet Union as Professor Pickering. It occurred also to Evgenia Ivanovna that now she could return to Stratonov the little ring he had given her and from which, unaccountably, she had never parted.

They were to start out the next day and in the meantime, at any rate, there were no obvious reasons why Stratonov should not make an excellent guide. Then on the pretext of showing off his knowledge of the language, but in fact in an attempt to establish the character of their relationship on the journey Stratonov asked Evgenia Ivanovna in French whether Mrs Pickering had been in Russia before. Evgenia Ivanovna exercised her right as a foreigner not to reply to indiscreet inquiries.

During the journey to Kakhetia Stratonov kept to French so as not to give the Englishman any food for suspicion. Now, in their private conversation in the Zinandalipark, Stratonov's French could of course be explained only by his passionate desire to keep up the pretence. It was a clear plea for mercy... Suddenly the banging which had shattered the Alazan night stopped in the darkness behind them: the driver had managed to make himself heard and somebody was coming to meet them. A lantern flickered in an invisible hand, lighting up a pair of feet in thick Caucasian socks.

'Success,' said Stratonov. 'We can get in at last . . . Can you see, or may I offer you my arm, Mrs Pickering?' His voice was at a slight distance. He came nearer. Evgenia Ivanovna's in-decision was almost audible in the midnight silence of the Alazan valley. She touched his arm, perhaps out of politeness, and to-gether they picked their way towards the house.

The night was disturbed. The Englishman needed warm com-presses, but there was no hot water. The way of life of the new world was Spartan indeed . . . a small bottle that once had held 'drops of the Danish King' was found in a medicine-chest and some old powders of the same regal origin, a legacy from the former owners of the Zinandali palace. Half the night was spent in massage and the rubbing in of liniment and then the attacks ended as abruptly as they had come, and did not return.

Evgenia Ivanovna wakened late next morning. Half asleep, she looked round the room with its raspberry-coloured wallpaper which she had not noticed the night before in the candlelight. It had the look of a neglected throne room of a monarch who has fallen upon evil times – but through the open door the garden was fresh and green and its fragrant air streamed into the stuffy room. In his dressing gown and with a book in his hand, her husband was sitting, quite recovered now, looking even taller and thinner than usual.

The young woman stretched herself and felt newborn in this vast four-poster bed with its steps and its drapery, designed for the passions of an unknown ruler; Evgenia Ivanovna's life had barely begun. She saw a blissful eternity stretching ahead of her – a sweet numbness spread over her body; to touch its satin smoothness amazed and delighted her. Enjoying every second with eyes half closed, she amused herself watching her husband until she suddenly remembered Stratonov lying on a couch on the floor below, a cigarette between his teeth, his eyes insolently scrutinizing her nakedness through the ceiling, the carpets, the very sheets.

The half-conscious realization of Stratonov's proximity pursued Evgenia Ivanovna the rest of the morning: sleep alone could rid her of it, so she returned to sleep. And indeed at first Stratonov vanished as soon as her eyelids closed, but then very soon he found her again, and, against her will, embraced her with his whole being, a man transformed and without any of the shortcomings which she had tried so hard to notice the night before. And they became so close that it was impossible to distinguish where he ended and she began. . . . Suddenly the bedroom grew the size of a square, packed with people; the bed, now looking like a hearse, moved through the crowd, that parted to let it pass and pretended not to notice what was happening.

She woke with a cold, tickling sensation in the feet, the blanket had slipped to the ground. Two roses that had not been there before lay on the night table beside the bed. Mr Pickering, in the same position, only by now fully dressed and shaven, sat in the same place by the open door with a book on his knee; the rice pages were stirred gently by the breeze from the garden. While Evgenia slept he had managed to get through the history of Kakhetia from the capture of Agsartan the Second to the misfortunes of Teimuraz the First. As prescribed in all love stories, the poor monster was watching over its beloved, completely unaware that it was being robbed.

Conscious of some movement, it tiptoed towards the bed.

'You struggled so violently in your sleep, Jenny,' said Mr Pickering, leaning against the carved bedpost, 'as though you were being pursued. . . . I came over to you twice.'

Evgenia Ivanovna was horrified by her husband's words. 'I had a bad dream,' she nodded, pulling the blanket up to her chin. 'Why didn't you wake me?'

'By the time I got to the bed you were already smiling. . . . I decided it was over. What was pursuing you, my darling?'

There was no hidden meaning in his voice, only an insinuating tenderness, which to the sinner caught in the act can appear the most dangerous trap of all.

To tell the truth was out of the question so Evgenia Ivanovna sought protection in the first falsehood that came to her mind. She didn't even have to pretend very much, she had thought recently of her mother's death, which she believed was not unconnected with the silver candlesticks and her father's golden watch, a present from his colleagues which she had illegally buried in the orchard. And she embroidered the story and babbled of that memorable day when an official had dug up half of their property searching for the wretched valuables.

'Mamma's tomatoes were still growing on the beds. . . .'

The Englishman interrupted his wife in the middle of a sentence:

'Don't go to all that trouble, Jenny. . . . Repeating one's dreams is like unfolding smouldering paper; they fall to pieces!'

In her fear of losing her husband's trust, and to allay any suspicions he might have had, Evgenia Ivanovna made a clumsy attempt to draw him to her. The Englishman gently unclasped her arms round his neck, and she understood that although her husband had no desire to inquire into the nature of the unfaithfulness that had in fact never taken place, at the same time he wasn't attracted by the dregs of love left by another man. In her despair that she might have uttered a name in her dream Evgenia Ivanovna burst into tears. Repentance tied her into knots, and threw her in hysterics against the pillow. With one hand crushing the rose that happened to be there, the Englishman waited for the end of the tears with a glass in his other hand. Her nightdress had slipped from her shoulder, the childish tears fell on the naked breast. Nothing could have convinced him more of his wife's innocence than this small display of shamelessness.

When the sobbing died away, Mr Pickering took Evgenia Ivanovna gently in his arms.

'Calm yourself, Jenny, you mustn't be afraid, relax with me. I'll always understand. . . . Drink some of this water,' he said, putting a reassuring hand on her quivering shoulder. 'Never mind what happens, however bad it is, I will never hurt you, so don't worry, yes, relax, like that. . . . Incidentally, can't you smell something delicious to eat in the air? It smells wonderful to me. It isn't in vain that in ancient Israel when Noah came safely aboard, God was represented as nostrils inhaling sacrificial smoke. At luncheon I will tell you a remarkable story, which took place, by the way, quite nearby, about one hundred and thirty kilometres to the south from here, by the meridian . . . but do get dressed quickly now: You've chosen a veritable glutton for a husband, my love!'

Stratonov knocked at the door for the second time. Unfortunately breakfast was long since past, but in Kakhetia people dined early, as the peasants do. Half an hour later all three of them passed through the suite to uninhabited reception-halls to the dining-room. The exhaustion of the past night was beginning to tell, conversation dragged, in spite of an abundance of wine and of the presence of the director of the Sovkhos, an acknowledged leader of the republican wing. Only when they were nearly finished did the meal become more animated, when the Englishman paid tribute to the excellent meal they had had. He wondered at the sophistication of such a meal in such a remote spot where the guests were so few and far between. Flattered by the approval of a connoisseur the director informed them that the cook's name was Cote, and he was on the point of providing a short biography of the artist, when he was called away to the farm. It was the height of harvesting-time in the whole of Kakhetia. During the quarter of an hour that he was absent, Stratonov informed the guests in confidence that the authorities from Tiflis came to this culinary paradise in order to strengthen their constitutions for the decisive battles for mankind – and it seemed as he was saying this that sand ground between his teeth. A tiresome battle of words between Stratonov and Mr Pickering occurred directly afterwards, only to be explained by the desire of each to outshine the other in the eyes of the woman they loved. Out of the corner of her eye, without turning her head, Evgenia Ivanovna went on watching her irritated guide. After the adventure of the night before, the living Stratonov seemed to her almost like a corpse. Opposite her at the table sat an unkind man who had not had enough sleep, and who was no longer a young man at all. No one had tried to shoot him in the ravine which Evgenia Ivanovna had seen in her dream, but rather some-one had punched him on the jaw which was why the lower part of his face kept automatically moving to the left. To compensate, perhaps, for his lost youth he had let his hair grow in a poetic style and it might have even suited him had it seen more warm soapy water. Coarse hands, shabby cuffs with safety-pins instead of cuff-links, the nervous exhaustion which could be sensed at a distance – all this told the whole story of Stratonov's existence. He lived an empty lonely life, without hope, without a woman who loved him, in the outrage of constant fear. Evgenia Ivanovna saw it all, and none of the bitter details brought her any relief.

Picking at a bunch of grapes Stratonov talked on the history

of the Zinandali estate and of the former owners of the present
State wine factory, the famous Chavchavadze family. He told
with particular relish the story of the men of Shamil who exactly
seventy years ago had poured down here from the mountain and
flowed back in clouds of smoke with two Georgian princesses
strapped to their saddles. Evgenia Ivanovna remained silent, and
it was clear to her that the guide was trying to fill in the time
allotted to him with this professional verbosity and abundance of
information so as to leave no gaps for personal questions or
explanations. He revealed, too, that at the end of the last century
the estate had passed from the bankrupt owners to the last
Russian dynasty and that Alexander III himself had slept in the
bed where the Pickerings had spent the night.

This information provoked an ill-advised joke from Mr
Pickering, who said that as far as he remembered Alexander was
the most outstanding Russian Tsar as far as size was concerned. . . . His eyes bowed over his plate, the guide remained
silent for a moment.

'During the lifetime of that Tsar foreigners refrained from
making ill-advised remarks on his behalf even at home, in
Europe,' he murmured softly and casually, as though quoting an
historical fact.

Evgenia Ivanovna found it so interesting to watch the rene-
gade's growing disarray that she decided not to remind him for
the time being how, soon after the February Revolution, the
same student Stratonov, boiling with anger against autocracy in
general, had told her anecdotes from the life of that same
Alexander: about his secret drunken orgies with his gardener,
his habit of carrying a flask of brandy in his leggings, about his
ridiculous solos on the trumpet.

The Englishman, in an effort to make peace, poured some
wine into Stratonov's glass.

'I had no intention to offend your political convictions,' Mr
Pickering said with sincere regret. 'I am myself even a little

taller than the man we have been talking about. People make fun of me at home in Leeds, saying that among all the professors I produce the most unforgettable impression upon the students, though not in the sense one would have chosen, perhaps.'

Stratonov found it more convenient to ignore the conciliatory manœuvre.

'I hope you will forgive the liberty I am taking which is quite outside my role as guide, but you know many visitors from the West are inclined to be flippant about our national tragedy.' He paused a second, then plunged on, foolishly imagining perhaps that by dangerously provoking her husband, he might raise his stock in Evgenia's eyes. 'And this doesn't prevent them from pilfering souvenirs from Soviet restaurants in the shape of palace napkins, for example, with the initials of the late Emperor on them. Obviously, in spite of all their enlightenment, there is still a demand in Europe for a good bit of rope from the hanged man's neck. . . . I admit, so far I haven't met this enthusiasm among your compatriots, but I'm perfectly sure there would be some of them who might care to spend a night or two in the Emperor's bed. . . .'

And without allowing the startled Professor Pickering time to collect his thoughts, the guide enlarged upon that particular kind of foreigner who comes to the Caucasus for the shooting, enjoys the marvellous wines, and then arriving home laden with gifts airs his views on the wholesomeness of socialism for Russia.

'What is so obvious, at the same time,' Stratonov went on, rising in his chair in a state of great agitation and hurrying to complete his rebellion before the director returned, 'is that not one of these firm friends has yet asked to come and live among us . . . I've said what I wanted to say . . . thanks for listening. Shall we go on with our work?'

Plans for a tour of the Alazan valley had already been worked out in Tiflis. The second part of the day was given over to the study of Kakhetian wine – its history, and production, and the cellars of the Sovkhoz. To prepare for the latter, most responsible part, they went for a stroll in the surroundings of the Zinandali palace. The Director himself took his guests into the gardens shaded by cedars and huge plane and Sterkullian trees.

Stratonov turned to the Englishman casually and asked him whether these ancient trees did not make him think of demons for ever on guard, waiting to clasp and crush any storm that came their way. Mr Pickering answered, with great reserve, that no, they didn't strike him that way. Then, from a burning need to obliterate the bad impression created by his outburst against the West, Stratonov, as politely as it was possible for him to be, asked Mr Pickering whether he had ever nurtured a scientific interest for the past of the Caucasus? No, the other one replied drily, he never had. . . . By this time they had reached the very edge of the Zinandali escarpment. Old chestnut trees, their fruit crunching underfoot, hung over the ravine; wild thorns, shrubs cascaded over the edge and down the stony sides. Far below the land flattened and wild cypresses grew – in the distance they could see the lilac edge of mountains.

'From here you can see the whole process from beginning to end,' Stratonov recited quietly behind them, again and again swearing to himself not to irritate his clients any more.

. . . The vintage had begun in the whole valley the day before – the wine matured a week earlier than usual that year. The guilt-conscious guide went on murmuring to the distinguished guests: didn't they think that everything was whispering that morning: the foliage, the water, even the birds? Only the carts overloaded with baskets of the new crop creaked lazily down below on the roads, and behind, on the other side of the garden, the pressing machines hammered at full force on the wet cement floor. Pointing to the destructive calenders, where the noble beauty of the grape was dying in order to acquire the drunken wisdom of wine, Stratonov instructed his travelling companions in the difference between the types of Budeshere and Muvan, in the peculiarities of the March pruning of the vines; Evgenia Ivanovna caught a scornful smile between the vine growers when he began to enlarge upon the advantages of the grafting to the Berlandieri vine in the black earth regions.

Suddenly the elder one of them, a Georgian with a heavy brow and hands wet to the elbow with tomorrow's wine, ladled out a glass of foaming juice and handed it to the lady guest – an ancient mountain tradition was reflected in his slow gesture. Her eyes sparkled in response, her prettiness for a moment was transformed into dazzling beauty, she carried the glass to her lips and threw back her head, so that her short hair fell on her shoulders and her throat gleamed pink and naked; she swallowed the wrong way and a few drops missed her mouth, this amused her and she laughed. And saluting the eternal woman the old man touched his swirling moustache with the tip of his fingers, while she drank. . . .

It is doubtful if a glass of flat vine juice merited such spectacular admiration. Obviously the woman was aware of her beauty and of the effect she was producing. Glancing anxiously at his wife, and gradually beginning to understand Stratonov's role, the Englishman confusedly asked himself whether he himself had not become for Evgenia Ivanovna the weapon of revenge, the cruelty of which was sharpened by his appearance. When he started on his journey to her country, he couldn't have foreseen this humiliating competition with an inferior Russian gentleman and the insult of it consisted in the fact that there was no possibility of avoiding it now.

Evgenia Ivanovna caught her husband's glance fixed on her.

'It is quite harmless, quite non-intoxicating the way it is now, try it, darling!' – she was justifying herself and handed him the glass with some wine still left in it, and a scarlet rim from the touch of her lips.

Drawn into the game against his will, the Englishman drank down this unborn wine, harsh and burning though it was for him – he drank it and never took his eyes off his enemy, who was unconcernedly slashing his legging with a whip. Their eyes met and each knew there was a struggle close ahead of them, and that one of them would win, and the other would have nothing. And as though fixing the spot for the inevitable duel, Stratonov announced to the guests that an autumn church festival, followed by a yearly fair, was going to take place the next night in the village of Allah Verdi, on the opposite shore of Alazan. Representatives of all the Caucasian tribes, even the far-away Lesghins were coming to it. It would mean twenty kilometres of hellishly dusty, often bumpy, roads to get there but the miseries of the journey would be amply repaid by the abundance of exotic impressions.

'Oh, that sounds familiar to me. . . . Allah Verdi, Alaverdi,' – adopting the right accent, the Englishman remembered. 'It is on the old route where the Asiatic hordes at some time or other used to make their way to the south-west of Europe. As far as I remember there is an ancient temple there, founded by a pious wanderer. . . .'

'You have learned your morning lesson perfectly, Mr Pickering,' Stratonov loudly approved, because he had noticed the Oxford textbook on the Englishman's table in the morning. 'The temple was built by Father Joseph, one of thirteen monks brought here by Simon Stolpnik from Antiochia.'

'What did you say? Stolpnik?' the Englishman interrupted on a word he didn't understand.

'Oh, that is Stylites,' Evgenia Ivanovna explained to her husband, and reminded him of the same-named poem by Tennyson with her husband's favourite quotation: 'Show me the man hath suffered more than I.'

Without any particular need and again hardly only for her husband's sake, she fluently recited the whole stanza. There years before in the bay of Mod she hadn't known a word of English. Meanwhile Stratonov, with a faint smile, rubbed a spot on his sleeve, and the Englishman, admiring and holding Evgenia Ivanovna's hand made intimate marital passes over her.

'As we are on the subject, may I pick your brains with an old problem of mine,' continued Stratonov, smiling innocently at the Englishman. 'It says in my book that the Alaverdi temple was built in the seventh century, while Stylites lived in the fourth and fifth. Besides, in the middle of the sixth century, Khosroi the Great devastated Antiochia so thoroughly that it is unlikely that after such handling the country was able to send her missionaries abroad or even to support Christian teaching within her own frontiers. Do you see my problem?' And very patiently he explained to his enemy the discrepancies in the dates. 'I just don't understand – can you help me?'

The Englishman's ears grew a little red, automatically he picked a red berry from the yew tree on the path beside him and he thought for a minute, trying to make up his mind whether Stratonov was genuinely interested in obtaining information or whether he was merely putting the Englishman's knowledge to the test.

'There was no need for Antiochia to send missionaries here after Khosroi,' he began. 'At that time the Christianization of Georgia had been roughly completed. In the sixth century Prokopi of Cesarea described the Georgians as rabid Christians. Therefore, this monument could have been erected not later than in the fifth. Your book says – the seventh? The cheapness of a book no doubt raises its demand among the population, but . . . I would recommend you to buy English textbooks, we don't economize on authors of that calibre, nor on proof-reading . . . and perhaps even on paper. Incidentally, do you keep by you a *vade mecum* or do you have to come here often because of your job?'

The other man bared his white teeth, not all of them sound, in a comparatively frank smile.

'Kakhetia is not included in tourist itineraries because of the lack of well-equipped bases, as you discovered last night. Is that what you mean?'

'No ... I was interested to know, Mr Stratonov, whether you dabble in history in your spare time or whether your company demands from its employees a special knowledge for the job ... which you perform in so original and inadmissible a manner?'

The conversation had turned to French in order to observe equality in weapons, then suddenly Russian speech burst out again.

'I serve ...' Stratonov was now angry, 'and my services are paid for by you in foreign currency which is very valuable to us; we are still very poor. ... As you know, our Allies didn't share the spoils of victory with us, though in fact it had been bought with a sea of Russian blood ... My little stream is included in it, too. You see, for the building of a new Russia we need a lot of money ... among other things for the replacement of my shoes, which are on the point of collapsing completely under your very eyes, Mr Pickering!' Now he was unable any longer to control himself and stop in time. 'Anyway, when Russia's Allies abandoned her in her distress. I was forced to leave my country for a while ... until I decided to return and do something constructive to help, even if it were only draining swamps. To do that I had to stifle my soul, and to betray my dreams, even to behave like a brute so that now I can hardly bear to remember the things I did. ...'

There was something naïve and stilted about his monologue that seemed to hide a deeper, unexpressed guilt. His cheeks were flushed, his speech was jerky, betraying an inner wretchedness that words dared not express. Mr Pickering, equally wretched, turned to his wife, for whose sake he had been suffering truly Russian tortures all morning. Holding a small mirror in her palm Evgenia Ivanovna was applying lipstick – her hand trembled and a ray of sun danced on her pale cheek.

'I suspect,' she said, without interrupting her occupation, 'that

Mr Stratonov has launched into this inappropriate confession for the benefit of a third person who is not with us.'

The lipstick had gone blunt and she threw it into the bushes.

The moment passed but each knew the tragic dénouement was only deferred for a while. They walked on silently, elaborately enjoying everything they passed, until they arrived back at the spot they had started from. It would have been hard to find a better place to harbour some sweet, poetic secret and sure enough, in the wild tangle on the edge of the Zinandali plateau, a white stone summerhouse lay hidden, a little summerhouse with a cupola, the memory of which, Stratonov assured them, was worth carrying back with them to England.

He stood square against the summerhouse, screening the doorway. 'Here,' he began shakily, 'is one example of what happens to these dreams of ours. Perhaps one shouldn't attempt to share it with outsiders but I think it confirms something Mrs Pickering was implying, that to regret is not enough. One has to see what happens to the ruined dreams. There is a legend that the poet Griboyedov became betrothed on this very spot. His bride belonged to the Chavchavadze family; her name was Nina, and she was only fifteen. Unfortunately, because of its tempting seclusion, not everyone has treated this romantic trysting place with the reverence that is its due.'

With an air of establishing a piece of painful evidence, the guide moved aside and the guests remained frozen on the threshold, with horrified exclamations of anger and amazement. The floor of the summerhouse was evenly polluted to the last centimetre, even in the corners, a reminder of the constancy of human habits and the advantages of persistent training. The chalky walls that remembered Nina's innocent whispers were covered with obscene drawings and inscriptions. Imploringly Evgenia Ivanovna squeezed her husband's elbow. Turning round in fury, Mr Pickering kept his eyes lowered to the shabby cotton tie of the guide.

'I promised my dear wife,' the Englishman uttered with icy wrath, 'to conceal from the authorities in Tiflis your impertinent and pathological behaviour. We would both be equally loath to think our visit to your country should be the cause of any further misfortune for you.'

With an old-fashioned gesture the Englishman offered his arm to his wife, and the livid Stratonov barely had time to get out of their way.

Luckily, on their way back, the director reappeared and hurried to remind them of the practical details of their tour; next they were to visit the underground storeroom of Zinandali. Taking the reticence of the Englishman as a symptom of another bout of sickness, he offered to test the medicinal effect of the heady Alazan treasures on the foreign ailment. With his acquiescence Mr Pickering showed great tact and understanding of universal hospitality. Accompanied by Stratonov who was reduced now to an almost obsequious respect, the three of them descended into the vaulted cellars where in the chill spicy darkness one of the subtlest fragrances of the earth is born. But it must be said that neither the gigantic barrel, three times man's size, the original of all Zinandali barrels, nor the long fermented samples from the encrusted bottles themselves, nor the obvious repentance of the guide – could improve the temper of the sensitive guest. It was true that obeying the imploring looks of his wife, Professor Pickering abandoned his original plan to leave for home at once, but he very firmly declined the invitation to visit the fair in Alaverdi, on the pretext that a sleepless night in the open would not suit him. At ground level again, still arm in arm with his wife, he retired to their quarters, and in two hours and a quarter they sat watching from behind lowered blinds, exchanging brief remarks from time to time on the events of the day.

It was a golden day, even for Kakhetia. In the distance, a mountain glacier glinted in the sun like the blade of a knife fashioned from translucent lilac stone. Clouds drifted calmly above it, and watching them Professor Pickering forgot his fury with Stratonov. To return to Europe the way they had come would mean lengthy and difficult conversations with Moscow. Towards the end of the day when the Director, splendidly un-aware of any crisis, went again to see his guests, Evgenia Ivanovna had managed to persuade her husband he had been the unlucky victim of her country's unsolved political conflicts. And to cap it all the guilty Stratonov had sat half of the day in the boiling sun with such a woebegone expression on his face that in the end Professor Pickering's heart melted and he agreed to see the trip through to the bitter end.

When the time came for the trip to Alaverdi, round the corner of the main building came their vehicle, the same ancient, rattling, shuddering, open-topped machine they had travelled in before. After the loading of carpets, wine and various foodstuffs, a small water-tank was fastened with wire to the luggage carrier, in case, God forbid, something should happen to the valuable head of Mr Pickering.

When the car moved, the last to jump in the front seat was the visibly reduced and speechless Stratonov.

The motor car allotted to the guests by the authorities during their stay in Georgia had once upon a time been the apex of technical achievement and according to legend the Viceroy of the Caucasus himself had driven in it. Time and possibly frequent struggles with the mountain tops had turned the frail foreign Buick into a native 'Biuk' hardened in adversity. The un-initiated feared to use it as a means of conveyance, but as soon as they realized that there was no alternative they instantly dis-covered the attractive side of travelling in it, as one does in every puzzling undertaking.

On the battered seats two wine distillers from the neighbour-ing Teliani were already awaiting the guests. In the round,

scarlet optimistic face of one of them one could detect an inclination for the delights of the flesh, whereas the ascetic appearance of the other pointed on the contrary to an adherence to
spiritual matters. As they said themselves, like Martha and Mary,
they complemented each other in the responsible task conferred
on them by the Tiflis authorities – to display a truly Kakhetinian
hospitality to the honoured British guests. Mr Pickering, judging
by their severe demeanour, first took them to be local ministers,
a fact which rather paralysed communication between them, but
the unusual experiences on the journey brought the passengers
closer together with every kilometre. They were jolted equally
high over the pot-holes, they rolled together on the steep descents
and occasionally shared together the few comfortable moments
when they leaned back against the leather cushions, waiting, by
experience, for the next series of squeaks and jerks. And so that
time should not hang heavy on them, either the driver changed
gears with a crack denoting breakage, or the radiator began to
boil and the tethered wooden cork on the top shot up as out of a
champagne bottle, after which the driver attempted again such
daring on the corners that the body for a short time lost its
ponderability as well as its pulse and any hope for a better future.

To the Englishman's delight the two wine merchants proved
to be such excellent, uncomplicated characters, gay, proud,
guileless, that he soon forgot the recent provocation. Half-way
out the more corpulent one kept shouting into Stratonov's ear to
overcome the horrible clatter of the car.

'Translate to him, my friend, to give him an idea. The whole
valley, one hundred and fifty versts – nothing but wine . . . wine
mixed half and half with fire flows in the veins of Kakhetia.
Napareuli – you've seen it on the bottles? – is to the left behind
the river, where you see the horse. Gurdzhani, Kardanakhi –
you've heard of them? . . . they are farther away, past those
white gates beyond the cypresses. You can travel the length and
breadth of Alazan to the tinkle of glasses. If he wants some, all he

has to do is write straight to me: The World, Georgia, nothing more, just my name. We'll send the best we have, the one we drink ourselves at weddings. Be a good soul, "Katzo", translate my name to him!'

Stratonov translated, excited, adding ideas of his own here and there and purposely making mistakes, so that he had a reason to turn to Evgenia Ivanovna for help. He was sitting with his back to her, with a sheep on his lap, but the whole way she was tormented by the feeling that he was staring at her, pleading her forgiveness. A cool breeze began to blow from Alazan and there were fewer roads. Now they all joined into one road that looked like the dried-out bed of a river had it not been chopped up in narrow gauges leading to the lilac slopes of the mountains. The Buick began to pass more riders on the way: sometimes they were two in a saddle. They passed ox-carts carrying whole families. The head of the family walked by the side, the old people shuddered and shook on the front of the cart while inside from behind the curtain of carpets flashed the black eyes of the numerous offspring. Everyone went to the fair, the dogs remained at home. The car horn having long since gone hoarse, the driver proceeded without it with enthusiastic shouts and gesticulations.

The snow covered mountain ridge came closer. . . . Night was falling. . . . Conversation grew slack. The evening was rushing to meet them, the cypresses moist from the early mist drooped over the sides of the road. A breath of manure-smelling smoke wafted in the cool air and the doomed lamb began to show an understandable anxiety; the thin distiller rose and touched it with his hand, as though invoking it to wisdom. Suddenly from behind the trees the stern cube of the Alaverdi temple appeared, its slate roof shining pink in the setting sun.

Stretching their limbs and losing the thread of their conversation they walked out on to the trampled maize field. Somewhere near, in the twilight, one could hear the din of the camping fair, like a horde on the march. A fine dust, gritty to the teeth, hung in the air. Stratonov put his hand into his pocket to take a handkerchief and wipe his face and something glinted as it fell out on to the ground. He managed to put his foot on it but not before Evgenia Ivanovna recognized the empty lipstick case which she had thrown in the grass of the Zinandali garden. The incident unexpectedly excited her, provoked her to mischief.

'I pray that you should love this land, our generous old mother; Kakhetia is yours, may it live for ever!' exclaimed the fat distiller and kissing his fingers he put them piously to the thin dust under his feet.

While the carpets were being spread around the mulberry-tree and the driver distributed the lamb stew with great formality, the humble Stratonov took the guests to see the cathedral. By agreeing to accept Stratonov's further services, the Englishman was showing the extent of his affection for his wife and together they pushed and jostled their way through the stream of humanity that flowed into every corner of this 'mushroom' town – with the stream they were drawn past the unharnessed carts, the rows of tents like coloured pebbles of rare design. Everywhere they looked gastronomic delights, crackling like their Georgian names, were bubbling in cauldrons, on braziers or strung up on rods that spurted flame in the growing dusk. In the tents bales of the still hot pudgy *churek** reached to the ceiling – and everywhere there was the local wine, in pitchers, in goat or buffalo skins, in slanting bottles of ancient knobbly glass – it was waiting in the overflowing mugs – they had only to stretch out their hands. Mr Pickering lingered more and more at the booths, as if bent upon educational matters and noticing his interest in the local delicacies Stratonov began to purposely lose him in the crowd. Soon, at the other side of the fair, he looked back stealthily and satisfied himself that he had been successful.

* Flat Georgian bread loaves.

The market which had started the day before was now in full swing. The human stream pushed and jostled its way between great heaps of merchandise. There were bizarre speckled cotton prints from Moscow, still smelling of northern hay or Javel water, beside Kakhetian cloaks and handbags, while domestic utensils – from tinned pans that held half a sheep to water-jugs for the Georgian mud-huts – mingled with solid everlasting sweetmeats of magic colours concocted specially for young teeth. The potters of Telav, their heavy arms hanging between their knees, squatted beside their works of art – their children's toys and whistles with three piercing notes, and their huge narrow necked bottles buried in the ground with peasant wine. nearby the local saddlers sprawled on the grass, and watched proudly over their masterpieces; graceful saddles with pinch-back pommels, harnesses with enamel clasps made by the Lesghins, kuban bridles and belts in black silver, fit for Beka Opisari himself, and the most precious of Dzhigit dreams – slippers of mosaic shagreen with gilded heels, that clearly yearned for the foot of the beloved.

'Where is he hiding from us, your gaunt Professor, blast him!' – Stratonov kept repeating in a boy's falsetto, growing bolder every moment, feeling instinctively that Evgenia Ivanovna was caught, too, in the magic atmosphere of the fair. 'Give me your hand, I'll help you through the crowds. . . . God knows why I went into that derelict summerhouse last night; I'd never been there before. And also I keep forgetting to ask whether it is true that the great misfortune that struck Mr Pickering took place in Cairo or Bombay?'

'What misfortune? What are you talking about?' Evgenia Ivanovna called out, over the noise of the fair somewhat more affably than she ought to have done.

'You know better than I . . . I heard about it back in Tiflis. After all, it might have had a disastrous effect upon his brain!'

'I have no idea what you are talking about.'

'Wasn't he hit on the head with a stick during some colonial demonstrations?'

Deceived by the compassionate tone and crushed in the crowd Evgenia Ivanovna missed the moment to retort, and to put this beaten, half-forgiven gentleman in his place, and then it was too late; it was quite unsuitable to defend herself, to argue, or even simply to discuss any misfortune that might have befallen her husband at any time; it was particularly pointless as the latter never had any business with colonial affairs. Nevertheless she decided to explain that the concussion had occurred accidentally, from a home-made bomb intended for someone else and flung through a window, and instantly Stratonov agreed that for a gentleman a bomb was far better than a stick. Evgenia Ivanovna wanted to cry from the humiliation and the muddle and particularly from despair that the guide should have dared remind her of their former relationship with this impertinent remark.

'It isn't important what it was for, I expect he got into some trouble because of his youth. . . . Give me your hand, I'll help you. . . .' Stratonov shouted again and stretched out his own over the heads of the crowd.

On an incline in front of them rose the Alaverdi Cathedral of St George . . . And not giving Evgenia Ivanovna the chance to reply Stratonov showered such a quantity of historical data on her, that it seemed strange that such a lot could have happened on such a small spot in the universe. A cobblestone pavement, with a ditch in the middle, led to a gate imposing enough for a fortress. Her heels went to pieces and the overpowering impact of the past began to irritate her, she longed to get back to the simple crowd of gardeners and shepherds, to the singers and dancers, to the youths with their eagles' profiles and the stern girls with eyes like serpents who rocked holding hands in the double saraband of the Perkhuli dance, amidst the flames of the bonfires. A resonant pious twilight filled the church and as though out of respect for the silence Stratonov delivered his lecture almost into Evgenia Ivanovna's ear, but she knew perfectly well why he was doing it and not daring to retreat for fear of an ever-growing proximity she sensed by the cold breath on her cheek that he was inhaling the air that separated them with his nostrils and to conceal it gesticulated with his hands quite soberly, pointing with the feigned indifference of a guide to the stone pillars surrounded by flaming candles, or to the half-restored frescoes showing an elegant leg of a byzantine priest standing out in the darkness, or the painfully drawn face of Fedor Tiron, very like his own, bent over the arch with a sword in his hand. The old Georgian stone with the green streaks running through it could be seen through the Apostles and Prophets and lent them the enchanting vagueness of phantoms. Suddenly Evgenia Ivanovna asked Stratonov to speak more slowly – for Professor Pickering had finally caught up with them; she knew he was there without having to turn round. Still chewing on something, the Englishman tried to catch more the intonation than the meaning of what Stratonov was reporting, with downcast eyelids.

Evgenia Ivanovna removed a speck of dust from her husband's leather jacket.

'Judging by your contented expression I think you have had a good supper! What did you have that was so good?'

'Something that could have come straight out of the Bible with a stuffing like fire . . . and not to be forgotten in a hurry! Until tomorrow at least my innards will not be safe!'

'If it was something that looked like our "pelmeni", only larger and rounder, it may have been "khinkali", a very powerful dish if you're not used to it,' Stratonov explained, but the Pickerings found it unnecessary to pay any attention to this communication.

'The strangest thing, Jenny,' Pickering went on in an intimate, cheery fashion, 'is that we scientists, when we reconstruct the past, are apt to neglect the gastronomic side. But you know food can tell us so much about the historical evolution of taste, for example about foreign influence, the economic problems of food, and so on ... Well,' he now turned superciliously, with a question as though reflected through his wife to the guide: 'What other calamities did the brigand Shakh-Abbas cause in Georgia?'

A child's cry drew Evgenia Ivanovna to the other side of the cathedral, where a local christening was taking place. An ancient man, in a shabby lime-coloured cassock, who appeared to have come down from a fresco, was murmuring a prayer, while a byzantine deacon from the cupola accompanied him by way of a chorus. A crowd of relatives stood around the font surrounded by dripping candles. The flames danced in the draught and illuminated in the darkness an old wrinkled profile in a black shawl, an unshaven cheek of a shepherd against the background of a faded banner or the picturesque head of a patriarch, his chin pressed to his black and silver jacket. They all stared sadly at the yelling descendant as through the thick glass of centuries. Two other families with other urgent requirements, also led by their great-grandfathers, waited for their turn on the steps of the altar. The comforting, alluring magic of the ceremony threw a spell on Evgenia Ivanovna, until a sharp attack of nausea forced her to rush to the porch. There was nobody there, not even a beggar, only a few stars. And although the nausea passed with the first gulp of the night's damp freshness, Evgenia Ivanovna was aware of a new sensation in her body, and she raised her breast in an automatic movement, as though feeling its weight. Probably the tiredness after months of travelling, the bad food, the stuffiness in the cathedral, the smell of incense and wax and, it seemed to her, the smell of unwashed nappies had contributed to her state, possibly also the sight of the half-strangled chickens, the peasants payment for the ceremony, which the priest had dragged squawking in behind the altar.

In the meantime the mist had swallowed up the view of the

mountains, only Alaverdi was a blaze of light. The flame of innumerable bonfires played on the low clouds, the weather was deteriorating. From the porch all the noises of the night; the din of the feast, the bleating of the sheep, even the burr of the mosquito that had travelled miles for his share in the feast – all were part of the powerful contented hum of the fair. Somewhere, close at hand, came the resonance of the local *daira* whose plucking is like heart beats, and the mysterious melody of the *tari* laced itself into the rhythm and they were both joined by human voices.

Evgenia Ivanovna wandered alone sinking every minute deeper under the spell of the Alazan night which turned the mist of burning fat and smouldering branches to magic. The wheels of a cart rolled past her, then she saw a short Georgian with his black and silver jacket and dagger long enough to find the heart of a mammoth. Throwing back his winged sleeves he danced to the music of a hired band as if inviting the whole of the Caucasus to dance with him, then dashed like the wind into the crowd that parted to make way for him – and disappeared into the night. A tall 'Chechenetz' in a fur hat and carrying a dead sheep across his shoulders brushed so close to Evgenia Ivanovna that a heavy drop fell on her white shoe out of the sheep's horn. Only then did the men catch up with her.

It was not easy to find their chosen spot under the yew tree. The peasant natives were preparing the shashlik as if they were performing a ritual. A pungent, teasing smoke rose from the heap of smouldering coals. The mother-of-pearl reflections of the bonfire played on the sheep's skin, rolled up with the fur inside. When the grilled meat was taken off the spits everyone sat fakir-wise on the carpet round the tablecloth, and the wine came into its own. It was poured generously to the women and the children, for the love of the beloved, and also for England, and was poured in the hope that simple-minded winemakers and shepherds should prosper and most particularly it was poured for the guests who were to carry away on the soles of their feet the dust of the Kakhetian soil . . . and after every toast Stratonov drank stealthily to something known only to himself. In an interval in the toasting, one of the men brought out of the night a band of blind singers, the *mestvire*. Six men, with holes instead of eyes, emerged from the darkness as though strung on a spit. Each held on to the shoulder of the one in front; the leader walked jauntily, with head thrown back, feeling for the path with his stick. Brothers in distress, they differed only in age, one of them had a flute, another an instrument made of four reeds, chained with silver, the third had a sazandali, a kind of harp; the hands of the others were lost in the dark. Suddenly the first one stumbled against an empty pail – and it seemed as though a ripple of misfortune ran back through the chain and died away – the first one almost tumbled into the fire, the last remained unaware of what had happened. The singers were given a piece of meat on a fork and a glass of wine, and were invited to show their skill. The leader blew strenuously into his flute for a third of a minute then the puffed-out cheeks sank in and the leather ball under his arm began to sing like a human voice. The music was joined by words, the song was a long one.

Barely discernible on the verge of the night and because of the smouldering fire, the peasants, the women with children in their arms listened to the concert of the blind; the uncomplicated meaning of the song could be read on their stern faces. It could have been saying how wonderful the world would be if you added to it everything that was missing. Now knowing the language each of the guests put their own words to the music. Evgenia Ivanovna threw a cursory glance at Stratonov. Slightly drunk, he lay at some distance, beyond the carpet, his feet almost in the bonfire and his glance concentrated on the blue, running tongues of fire. She was suddenly overcome with a desire to see into his thoughts, though it would have been humiliating to listen to Stratonov's justifications for his behaviour in Constantinople. Putting aside the unfinished glass of *madjari*, a young wine, she leant on her husband's shoulder without changing her position.

'I want to know what my dearly beloved is thinking – am I allowed to delve into the secret places of his heart?'

He replied in an undertone, so as not to interfere with the singing.

'You remember I took you to see the Paris copy of *The Blind* by Breughel the Elder? You remember the six men like these, walking in single file. The first one stumbles into a ditch and his misfortune is instantly transmitted to the others – to each in a different degree. We've just seen the exact same thing here . . . This is what happens in art, Jenny. Physically, the world remains the same, but what the artist has to say of it, will affect each one of us differently.'

Then the Professor began to propound his ideas on the mission of art, which, he believed, consisted neither in the narrow reflection of life, nor in imitation or repetition of the original, for who could repeat or imitate the work of the Creator? No, the true role of the artist is to perceive the world with a special eye, and logically to trace to its beginning and original intention each strand of thought, each separate action.

'Artists need never fear the abstract: the very material they use, the way they use it, both will tell their story, both can be interpreted. This has happened before – there was a time when the universe itself was a mere idea, a stroke on a rough map . . . this formula may be unwieldy now but perhaps as humanity becomes more mature, the formula will shrink again to the dimensions of a line in poetry, a hieroglyph, a magic sign. The artist's task is to compress his inspiration into the shape of a seed, so that it may find its way into another human soul and be re-born and blossom there in all its original beauty . . . it's all quite simple! From which you can make the merciless deduction, my darling, that I'm hopelessly drunk . . . but never mind, never mind, I feel happy now, like God on the last day of creation.'

He spoke passionately perhaps in his longing to keep Evgenia close to him but she freed the hand her husband had grasped in his excitement. In words that were not quite her own she reminded him they would soon have to leave Alaverdi, and she wanted to see it all once again before the magic went with the morning light.

'Will you come with me...' she asked '... but we must throw a coat round your shoulders.'

The Englishman looked into his wife's eyes; they concealed nothing. All three of them knew the moment had come. The pathetic Russian gentleman on the other side of the fire hurriedly lit his pipe with a cinder from the fire.

'Oh, my dear,' Professor Pickering smiled courageously, 'I become more god-like every minute, but your request finds me in an intermediate condition! I have lost the use of my feet and my wings haven't grown yet! Perhaps Mr Stratonov would accompany you?'

Hearing his name, Stratonov automatically pushed his beer away and spilt it in the process: then he began searching for his hat as though he were unable to function without it. It was soon found: the driver had been sitting on it. A woman's heels moved across the carpet, upsetting the glasses. At the same time one of the natives lifted his glass in an untimely and prophetic toast! 'Let this wine increase in us the fire of life and extinguish it before the clouds of disappointment come.' After his wife had left, the Englishman stared for a long time at the dark liquid in his glass, as though forgetting what it was there for.

The driver gave a shout in Georgian to the blind men and obediently they dissolved in the river fog that had risen with the dawn.

* * *

The Alazan night was ebbing, the feast was confined now to a few central streets. The birds had wakened, and were whirling in the brightening sky; among the empty booths there reigned the clatter of every day – hammering and angry voices and the squeal of departing wheels. The camp was moving on. Here and there figures sprawled by the bonfire, sleeping off their drunkenness. The morning breeze picked up sheets of paper and wisps of hay and tossed them here and there among the trees.

Evgenia Ivanovna walked slowly to allow Stratonov to catch up with her, but the distance between them did not diminish. She then pretended to be interested in a group of stallkeepers noisily dividing their profits and Stratonov had to stop beside her. The red glow from a home-made torch emerging from an old preserve tin lit up the little knot of people and outlined Evgenia Ivanovna's profile. Her face wore a strange unaccustomed smile, the frightening smile of a person who knows and enjoys power over another human being, yet the swollen, bitten lips were helpless as always.

'It's almost daylight; I couldn't lose my way now,' she said hurriedly, afraid that the mad curiosity she felt for this man might vanish in a wave of repulsion and boredom. 'I had better go by myself and you stay with Mr Pickering. His ignorance of the language might be embarrassing.'

'Oh, ignorance of a language can create no discomfort for the rich. Money is the best interpreter of all.'

Evgenia Ivanovna looked stealthily at her companion who was clearly preparing for battle.

'You seem to think my husband is a financier . . . I understand your resentment of him. In the town where I was born, the presence of a samovar in a neighbour's house or a cloak lined with fox fur could make exactly the same class distinction. But Mr Pickering is not a rich man; he is only a scientist, and a famous one at that. Incidentally, has his latest work been translated in your country?'

She had not forgotten the loneliness in Constantinople, there was more pain in her than hatred. In the absence of his own,

Stratonov was forced to defend himself with other people's weapons, profiting by their owners' absence.

'I'll be glad to reply if you promise to be patient.'

'Oh, you have no idea how patient I can be, Mr Stratonov.'

Silence fell, during which the guide examined a branch he had picked from under his feet.

'Very well, but may we speak in Russian . . . I would find it difficult to put what I have to say into a strange language,' Stratonov began, very disturbed. The great men of Russia had long been prophesying for her a special historical mission . . . unique in the sense that it lacked the egotism so typical of the rest of Europe. This mission was the subject of violent discussion among generations at home and a source of amusement to many of our detractors abroad. 'Meanwhile there is no reason to smile . . . for this is a matter of the oldest universal human need – for peace, kindness and truth, that is, the establishment of a higher humanitarian order . . . we can call it the dream of a golden age. Untarnished by many contradictory definitions, ridiculed and betrayed so often through the centuries, the dream still burns in the hearts of . . . well, let us say of the poor! . . .' he stumbled over the word '. . . and as Europe has lately been able to see . . . it burns corrosively when necessary. At first the quenching of this insatiable thirst was left to the goodwill and paternal conscience of the monarchy, of the clergy and the higher authorities, but later through endless disappointments and delays, the poor, the lesser breeds decided to take matters into their own hands. I tell you all former revolutions are mere reconnoitring – the real battle begins today and tomorrow. This is what united us here today.'

With considerable eloquence, though of a classroom standard, Stratonov sketched for his companion the origins of the cherished dream. Omitting, for brevity, the period of antiquity, he outlined the upheavals of the European Middle Ages, and the peasant wars, linked the Reformation with the social crisis of

Christianity, 'when the plot of the rich against the poor . . . was completely revealed'; he talked of the Utopians of the modern era, whom he called 'the intellectual rebels against the darkness of the Kingdom of Heaven', and counterposed for that the Civitas Dei of Augustine and the Civitate Solis of Campanella, dazzling her with his Latin which slightly embellished his pompous insincerity, glossed over the edgy corners and thus, across the encyclopedists and early socialism brought Prometheus' fire to the headlines of a Bolshevik newspaper.

Evgenia Ivanovna smiled at him gently:

'Yes, indeed, if you have yourself in mind as part of this great movement, this is a great acquisition for the universe. We in Europe all count very much on you, Stratonov, that you won't do us a dirty trick.'

For about ten yards one could hear only the whistle of Stratonov's branch cutting off the heads of the grass growing by the road.

'Here in Kakhetia, they prepare shashlik very well and I am glad to see that under its influence your mood has somewhat improved,' Stratonov murmured. 'But this time you guessed wrong, Mrs Pickering, I didn't have myself particularly in mind, but the whole of Russia who is shouldering this heroic task the centuries have prophesied for her. In fact it is the same way to the stars, but unlike the old ways, across heaven – it leads by the shortest earthly route, the hard and straight way. It will demand sacrifices, but the inspiration of the past instills men with determination and insensibility to suffering.'

'You hope to survive once again?' Evgenia Ivanovna smiled wryly.

'Laughter is of course excellent for one's health, but I can foresee that one day Europe will get a shock.'

'Oh, you frighten me with your threats, Stratonov. What other terror have you got in store for us?'

At last the branch broke in Stratonov's hand.

'I'm afraid, Mrs Pickering, that English humour will not get you very far. This is not a question of threats but of education by the Russian example.'

'Forgive me, but I don't quite understand . . . Are you really suggesting that Europe would want to imitate the Russian example and I wonder why? But we have got away from our original subject – how does all this relate to my husband's book – why the long introduction?'

'Why?' Stratonov exploded under her glance, 'why, because *his* science about fragments of ancient pottery and people dead long ago can wait while the living smoulder and demand retribution, and while the still wet and bloody sweat of the war and revolution rests on Russia's brow – she has no time for your husband's work . . . And why should he want another laurel leaf in the wreath of universal recognition?' Suddenly frightened by his outburst, he stopped and remained silent for a while, his face buried in his hands in order to recover his composure. 'Forgive my outrageous behaviour, Mrs Pickering. I didn't sleep last night, I mixed my drinks and this is not recommended even for drunkards.'

'. . . Particularly when working,' Evgenia Ivanovna agreed with mild reproach. 'I know something of your biography, and therefore I can understand your attitude, but believe me, your masters are so suspicious that even if they saw your zeal, I doubt, if this would improve your situation. Let's talk of something else.'

The cold truth of what Evgenia Ivanovna said reminded him of the risks he was taking. It was true, he could only have attained his present position after a thorough screening, possibly with a public confession; the conditions of his obtaining work at all would have been harsh, to rule out any repetition of his mistakes. He should never have been discussing such matters with the wife of a foreigner and now would have to steer the conversation into the right direction in order not to compromise his awaited report of this nocturnal stroll. So, he went on, the briefest acquaintance with conditions in Russia over the last twenty-five years explained the Russian's passionate desire for social change: two military defeats one after the other, a degenerate upper class, darkness and hunger and drunkenness obscuring everything that was decent, a criminal war and an increasing gap between wealth and poverty – all this was sufficient to bring out the national temperament.

'This heroic determination to go forward whatever the cost raises my country in the estimation of honest people the world over,' Stratonov ended with the obstinacy of despair.

'I have listened to you with great interest,' Evgenia Ivanovna said in a conciliatory tone. 'Besides, you speak so eloquently that I suspect you must have written poetry at some time in your life . . . but you lack sincerity. I learned in Tiflis that your country is going ahead by leaps and bounds . . . but in your case, Stratonov, it has really happened a little too quickly . . . if you compare it to what you said less than twenty-four hours ago.' She remained silent while the poison of what she had said brought a flush to his cheeks. 'Besides, there are no more official receptions for us in Tiflis and we are hurrying back home for the new university term . . . so that I shall have no opportunity to mention your loyalty to the local authorities.'

. . . Dawn was breaking, the arrow-shaped rays of the sun behind the mountains were lightening the grey-green sky. Having exposed an alien and threatening idea in front of an imaginary Europe, exhausted, Stratonov kept silent, working out in his mind how long he and Evgenia Ivanovna had left to be alone together? Unfortunately for him it could well hold the new unavoidable painful explanation.

'You reproached me a moment ago for my ignorance,' Stratonov prevaricated, 'but I read the books of this remarkable man long before you ever met him. A certain young woman, from a town in the Steppes, whom I loved very deeply and who

I lost for ever through my own weakness and inferiority ... she could confirm that I told her about his discoveries in Nineveh – true, it was only from a newspaper article – one Christmas, the last of the old régime, on the eve of the Revolution. I remember it vividly: I had just got there straight from a Petersburg hospital.'

And in desperation, he rushed headlong into such a detailed account of their first meeting at the school dance, that Evgenia Ivanovna could not help but smell the scent of wax and smouldering fir and remember the blissful shyness she felt at being alone with this wounded hero with his exciting city ways. 'You know, even in my hospital bed I was amazed by his knowledge, particularly amazed by his talent for reconstructing the past on the basis of the most trifling of evidence. It seemed to me that only a contemporary could possibly reconstruct the everyday life of Nineveh in the brilliant way he did.

'He seemed to know the primitive life and the bustle of the narrow streets and the whole exotic background so well that one felt he must actually have been there. . . . From this point of view I must admit he has remained remarkably well preserved . . . I mean it quite seriously, Mrs Pickering, from Kakhulia himself to the head of the department we in Tiflis have all admired your happy relationship and have marvelled at his zest for life at his age, particularly comparing him to our own uncertain, bruised generation.'

Stratonov was carried away. He could not stop talking from a sense of his own inferiority, jealousy and helpless anger and everything he said fell in the air between them and evaporated before Evgenia Ivanovna's ironic, interested silence. The difference between them now was so obvious, the true reason for Stratonov's lashing out at a man he could not imagine as a rival so understandable that Evgenia Ivanovna refrained from defending her second husband. She said nothing, merely waited, watching the antics which proved Stratonov's disarray, a mixture of penitent despair and an unqualified admission of guilt, though he had not yet been accused of anything. . . . Then in an attempt to cover up his guilt, Stratonov began to extol some of the Englishman's obvious qualities, precisely those that are intrinsic in a gentleman and acquire a double entendre from exaggerated admiration, he did it with the indecently patronizing expressions that happy lovers use to compensate an absent husband for the inflicted loss and thus increase the delight of the robbery. Suddenly he collapsed, stopped and fell silent.

Just then they heard someone singing near them. Evgenia Ivanovna stopped and put her finger to her lips. Three elderly Georgian women, obviously friends though very unlike one another, all wearing the same headdresses ornamented with silver, chikta kopi, were sitting on a carpet, while their square, clumsy husbands loaded empty barrels on to a car; they sang in an undertone something for their own pleasure, now and then raising an eyebrow, or lifting a finger probably at memories of the irretrievable past. The fourth, the youngest one, wrapped in a black muslin shawl accompanied them on the *chonguri*.

'So where were you, Mr Stratonov?' Evgenia Petrovna said, moving on but not taking her eyes from the women as if she wanted to memorize what she had seen. 'You have been silent longer than you are supposed to be in your position. Do go on . . . but please avoid personal subjects, I beg you. Tell me how much wine is procured in the Alazan valley and what other monarchs are buried under this soil.'

'Wine is not oil and it would be more correct to ask how much wine is *produced*. Besides, in Russian you say buried *in* this soil.' Stratonov murmured between his teeth.

'Try to be tolerant with a poor woman who after all is not to blame for not having used her native language for so long,' Evgenia Ivanovna replied very softly.

Then, gritting his teeth and determined to fill the hour that remained before the departure, Stratonov doggedly continued his lecture, suggesting, for example, that the density of population in the mountains and the presence of great stocks of wine should contribute to the unification of the Caucasian people. The Alazan valley could serve very well as banqueting hall for peace congresses, there was enough wine to drown humiliation, to drink to victory. In reality, however, in spite of very strict laws, crimes of revenge were frequent here. The long memories for inflicted pain surprised not only the natives themselves but guests as well. Even women, observed Stratonov, became cruelly indifferent here to the moral tortures which were the fate of the unfortunate man who had unwittingly wronged them. He ventured the idea that some toxic microcosm which reopened forgotten wounds may have been diluted in the local water.

'In the course of the last twenty-four hours it is the second time that you mention your misfortunes, dear Stratonov,' – Evgenia Ivanovna laughed in a kind of patient amazement. 'But do tell me, have you really suffered so much in your life that you need constant sympathy, even from strangers?'

'There are some truly Russian sorrows, from which there is neither oblivion nor recovery,' he replied barely audibly.

'But are you sure you have done everything you can about it?' Evgenia Ivanovna remarked with an even more piercing smile and moved on ahead, allowing the guide to catch up with her when he had recovered from his confusion.

The path that led round the fair turned steeply towards the wasteland with a few trees growing here and there, whose character was not yet distinguishable in the early morning light. Stratonov caught up with Evgenia Ivanovna at the turning at the last booth that sold refreshments. Here he asked permission to leave her for a moment.

'In all civilized countries,' he joked nervously, 'the condemned are allowed a drink before the execution. I would like to exercise my right to that. Please don't be alarmed. Nothing will happen. I'm not likely to forget I'm on duty.'

Pulling out some crumpled notes, he made his way towards the booth and knocked on the shutter, which was raised and a sleepy apocalyptic creature in a hastily donned astrakhan hat peeped out. Stratonov emptied the glass mug, glanced at the sky and dropping some more money on the counter ordered a short drink. He waved aside the cake which the owner offered in fingers painstakingly previously wiped on a dirty sleeve – and returned to Evgenia Ivanovna, the frustration and misery temporarily effaced from his expression, but with anger bottled up in his soul.

He asked Evgenia Ivanovna if they shouldn't be turning back now for it had grown cooler and the Professor would be wondering where his wife had gone.

'He had no reason to do that. I didn't come away alone, after all, I came with you!'

'And what if he finds out who it is you're with?' Stratonov made an insolent move to come closer.

'He already knows all there is to know about us. Apart from anything else, a great man can always be recognized by the fact that after the first conversation it seems you've known him all your life... Anyway, Mr Pickering knew of your existence long before he saw you in Tiflis.'

'It says a good deal for his powers of penetration,' Stratonov remarked rudely on the brink of sarcasm. 'I think I've had one too many today, to drown my sorrows ... but don't condemn me without hearing my defence!'

'Really, you shouldn't make such a fuss of it, Stratonov,' Evgenia Ivanovna said very sincerely. 'It's true, I was surprised to meet you back here . . . but I'm not reproaching you. I simply took it for granted, with my innate credulity, that you were dead.'

His face twitched with pain.

'Oh, then I can understand my lady's disappointment, coming back to visit a few cherished graves. What a shock the poor girl must have had to see one of her most familiar corpses sitting perched, so to speak, on the marble tombstone, alive and kicking.' For the first time, his tone changed with emotion. 'But who knows whether it isn't the thousandth time that I'm dying here now in front of you!'

'You crazy man, how could you have had time for all that?' Evgenia Ivanovna smiled coldly.

'Oh, yes, I died of pain and grief when the army was destroyed, I died of humiliation in the cattle truck during the evacuation, of hunger when we were together, of shame for my very capacity for survival. I died every time I came back to you with empty hands, every time I met your eyes, that convinced me of the uselessness of my existence . . . Just tell me honestly, weren't you better off without me?'

'You are perfectly right if only in the sense that it is easier for a pretty woman to make her life abroad if she's alone,' Evgenia Ivanovna agreed in a low voice.

Her cheeks flushed deeply. She remembered a midnight walk with her husband in some famous slums in the Middle East; the Englishman had preferred to see his ancient monuments first by moonlight, when silence and the curtain of the night stifled the noise of cars, and concealed the modern background. . . . Their lack of knowledge of the town led them to a suburb of brothels. They saw a sordid staircase leading to a basement; the noise of a wretched string band came up to them and the wriggling shadows on the whitewashed wall, the swearing and the stench of burnt meat and flickering orange lights, told them they were on the threshold to hell. Suddenly a half-naked woman tore out of the door with a wail and threw herself headlong up the steps, boneless, her clothes flying round her, and then vanished into the darkness of the night. The Englishman grasped his wife by the elbow, or she would have been carried along by the rapid movement. There was little of the human left in the creature that had flashed past, but even in those few seconds, Evgenia

Ivanovna had recognized in the poor wretch her former Russian friend. Until a kind, pock-marked merchant from Tunis had rescued Aniuta, she had shared the same bed with her in Constantinople after Stratonov had left. After her second marriage Evgenia Ivanovna had spent hours in a kind of nightmare reconstructing this scar on her memory that healed slowly under the skin of oblivion. Ever since then there was something about life which she could not bring herself to trust, now for the first time she smiled secretly, knowing she was finally free.

Her flushed face was refreshed by the breeze coming from the Alazan river, very deep at this time of the year. The river appeared at once beyond the steep white bank on which a wild rose was still blooming. The pebbles crunched under her feet, their dull shine like serpent's skin. Evgenia Ivanovna pointed it out to Stratonov – he did not reply. They came back by a different path, which meandered among wild stones, washed there by the spring floods.

'What could I have offered you then except a double suicide? And how could I have taken you with me when all I had to look forward to was certain death in a ditch at the first frontier post?' Stratonov whispered. 'I was shot at hundreds of times.'

'And every time they missed?' Evgenia Ivanovna showed a natural interest.

'Oh, if that was all . . . From the day I was set free, I have been a cleaner, masseur, a speculator's stooge, a china mender, all sorts of things. I've been everything except a corpse. There was no place for me anywhere, a vagabond, if he has even an unfinished university education, will be an object of the deepest suspicion to a master who can hardly read. It's been the memory of you that has kept me going all these years. Don't worry, I wouldn't change anything if I could. . . . You will go away to-morrow and I shall stay here and drown myself in drink and probably die of it. And this night will not be repeated, just as life is not repeated. But I love you, I worship you like some men worship God, without any hope of return. I've heard your voice so many times since then, in the thunder of the hills, in the rustle of grass, or in the song of birds – you can sentence me to any punishment you like if it will help me forget you. . . .'

Tickled by curiosity Evgenia Ivanovna was reminded once again that in spite of the grey hair at the temples Stratonov continued to indulge in verses. She remembered vividly another school dance in April 1917, when the young officer, recovering from his wounds, recited his verses to the accompaniment of the piano on the iron manacles of autocracy, and banners bathed in blood.

'You should not be saying these things to me, Mr Stratonov,' she warned him severely, almost primly.

'Oh, it doesn't matter to me, nothing matters,' he repeated recklessly, as though from the bottom of a grave waiting for the earth to close in on him. 'No matter what happens you will remember the night we escaped until the day you die. Do you remember, we knelt silently . . . do you remember the old ladies who were crying as they blessed us with the holy images? I slipped the ring into the warm childish palm which closed forever. . . . God Himself sent you to me, in answer to all the prayers of all the mothers in my family . . . and no matter, no matter how life may have separated us, we were never parted for a moment after that night. In my attic in Tiflis there is a chair, on which no one is allowed to sit because when night falls it is you who sit on it. And I know in my heart that you are happy there . . . I'm not asking you to come with me, a beggar is satisfied with a dream. Now you'll not even be that. This is the last dawn that we'll ever share . . . Forgive me, Jenny, and may your precious name be blessed for ever.'

For greater conviction he ended his confession with a light, almost stealthy touch of her elbow and then Evgenia Ivanovna slapped his face, but not very hard because once again during the night she had had a fit of nausea. . . . In fact she slapped him quite gently, with sufficient force to shatter any illusions he might have retained about their relationship.

'You were wrong, Mr Stratonov, to call me by that name; only my husband uses it,' she reproached him in a firm voice, that trembled just for a moment.

Stratonov was unable to pretend that he had not seen what had happened. He was on the point of thanking with a stilted little bow the smart foreign lady who had, in doing what she had done, liberated him from further qualms – but he did not have the time. Evgenia Ivanovna's discomfort revealed itself in the most natural way, so that it was not the slap on the face but precisely the moment that followed it which proved the most painful one in Stratonov's punishment. The attack of nausea became insurmountable, rose to Evgenia Ivanovna's throat, threw her down on her knees, as she managed to stagger a few steps away from the guide. In spite of her attempt to control it, pressing her hand to her mouth, the vomit burst through her fingers. They had eaten spicy and unusual food that evening, but that was not the reason for the sickness. Without words, the incident explained to Stratonov that the future mother of an English child could not have behaved in any other way.

When Stratonov, having turned away in embarrassment, ventured again to look at Evgenia Ivanovna, she was still on her knees, wiping her hand with a bunch of local blue wormwood.

'It's all so sudden, I'm so sorry . . . I've got a handkerchief somewhere there . . . will you give it to me?' she asked in a pathetic, jerky manner, trying to overcome the sickness, while Stratonov remained at a distance and searched with paralysed fingers in her handbag. 'Yes, that's it, thank you . . . and at the same time take the ring, your old ring, it's at the bottom of the bag wrapped in paper. I was going to return it to you before I left . . . but it doesn't matter, take it now!' – and before the nausea swept over her again, she apologized for the trouble she was giving.

Echoing her tone, Stratonov, completely lost now, murmured that it was no trouble at all, it was his duty to do what he could, and to spare his clients any discomfort, that he wished he had something to fetch water in. But she interrupted him.

'Never mind, I'm all right, we'll be home soon. Only please turn away now! . . .'

Whilst she rose to her feet behind Stratonov's back and wiped and shook out her clothes, he could not tear his eyes away from the cold, dull gold circle in the palm of his hand which he had himself once upon a time slipped on the woman's fourth finger.

'May I offer you my arm?' he asked in the voice of a stranger.

'No, thank you, I can manage. I feel better now . . . but let us go quicker, please, I am so tired . . .'

They went back across the fields; the sun had risen unnoticed, the day promised to be grey.

'I shall take a wonderful memory away with me of this trip to Alaverdi,' Evgenia Ivanovna said with a sigh as they walked on. 'Tell me, is this fair repeated every year?'

The question was put in French, and with it Evgenia Ivanovna closed the incident for ever and consigned to oblivion the long drawn out misery both of them had felt. Experience had long since taught Stratonov the courage to bear the blows life dealt him; somewhere along the way, like many another failure, he had acquired the knack of telling himself that things might have been worse still. But nevertheless he felt a pang he'd never felt before for how was he to fill the emptiness in his soul now this last pain had been removed.

'Yes, the traditional autumn fair takes place here on the Holy Cross Day,' Stratonov, adapting himself to the new situation replied in the loud tone that guides adopt for the comfort of absent-minded or slightly deaf tourists. 'By means of strong anti-religious propaganda . . . sometimes using not only educational methods . . . the religious fanaticism of the local population is channelled into this ordinary peasant festival. I am very happy that the enchantment of this rather exotic entertainment has reached both you and Mr Pickering. . . .' And the short lecture ended with a catalogue of the local handiwork sold at the Alaverdi fair.

On the way back, Stratonov lagged behind on the pretext of gathering brushwood for the bonfire. It was strange that the Englishman seemed not to notice the sudden re-appearance of his wife. In her absence the natives had succeeded in putting a black felt cap on the foreign visitor's head, thereby elevating him to the position of honorary citizen of Kakhetia. The gastronomic excesses of the night before had been followed by an orgy of mental exercises. Evgenia arrived at the tail-end of a discussion on the most important topic of the day. Mr Pickering was in complete agreement with his new friends that to live in the world in the old way was a very dangerous thing to do now that civilization had reached such an explosive point; progress would have to be governed by humanitarianism – he insisted, however, that the nobility of any idea was to be measured by the amount of good it brought the people, not by the number of victims martyred for its sake. . . . The conversation ran on a rather simplified vocabulary, but the lack of words was compensated for by vivid gestures, and a universal sign language which Professor Pickering with his well-tried powers of detection of hieroglyphs managed to decipher remarkably well. Added to which both sides had reached that blissful state of mutual understanding when wine successfully replaces the interpreter.

Perhaps this may explain Mr Pickering's immobility even when his wife slipped down beside him on the carpet. But although he went on nodding to his hosts with an air of absorption, his attention was entirely concentrated on the mysterious details which jealousy notices with such fatal precision, the drawn features of the face, the dust on his wife's skirt and the inexplicable disappearance of the guide.

'Mr Stratonov decided to gather some brushwood for the last

bonfire,' Evgenia Ivanovna replied in English to her husband's unspoken question. 'We went almost the whole way round the fair and then suddenly all I wanted desperately was to get home . . . darling, tell me, is our Leeds very far from London?'

'No, it's four and a half hours by train,' said the Englishman, unaware that his little round hat had gone awry and staring blankly at something in front of him.

'I've wanted to see London for a long time, I want to get to know the capital of my new country. We must go there, as soon as we're settled – yes? Is our house far from the University?'

'No, about twenty minutes walk. It's on Cottage Road.'

'Is there a park somewhere near us? . . . We will soon be needing one nearby, even if it is only a small one. . . .'

'The heath is only a few minutes away.'

'And as soon as we get back, we'll start our evening walks before going to bed. . . . We must do that. Are there any big trees or not? . . . Big trees are so peaceful. And I suppose there is a church, too?'

'Yes, quite near. It's called St Chad's.'

Worn out, Evgenia Ivanovna leant her head against the yew tree and closed her tired eyes. She tried to imagine herself five years hence but, strangely enough, did not succeed. Groping in the dark she pressed her husband's hand, but the cold hand did not respond.

'Darling . . . I'm sure I shall be quite good at housekeeping. And because my own mother is dead I will love yours twice as much . . . Is that correct English?'

'No, in English you only have to say I shall love her,' Mr Pickering corrected still hesitatingly.

Nobody could hear them; about twenty feet away men were busy pulling at a body lying on the floor of the Buick, trying to retrieve the driver from a state of blissful unconsciousness and back to a world of trouble where man had to work and cars were for driving. Suddenly Evgenia Ivanovna pressed her tired body to her husband's.

'Let's go home, I beg you, tomorrow if we can. I don't feel well here, I can't stand it any longer.'

His shoulder trembled under her cheek.

'Are you ill, Jenny?'

'I don't know, I know nothing . . . but I think there will soon be three of us.'

This news had to be repeated to Mr Pickering twice before his feeling of loneliness finally gave way to the solemn realization of momentous change. The shadows of bitterness disappeared from his face slowly, never to return. He carried his wife's hand to his lips and keeping it in the air, lovingly examined her large, moist, honest fingers.

'Tell it to me again, in Russian, please,' he asked for the third time.

Stratonov returned and throwing handfuls of brushwood on to the fire, retreated before it leapt into life. Everybody sprawled on the carpet again and watched the dancing flames. For a time Stratonov on the other side of the fire remained practically invisible to the Pickerings. The guide sat, his head bent, on the driver's carpet, staring at a mound of stones with grass growing between them, left after road repairs. A stone at the edge of the pile, by a mysterious coincidence, had the shape of a heart. He felt inclined to take it away with him in memory of this night. It came out easily from its earthen bed. At the bottom of the hole a black monster stirred, and raised a sinister head. Brusquely Stratonov returned the stone to its place, and then began with some embarrassment to prepare for departure. He rolled up the carpets, put the empty bottles and the unwashed crockery into the boot. He did it all efficiently, without hurrying, which showed both his repentance and his experience.

Then suddenly it was all over and time for the Pickerings to say good-bye. News of the foreign visitors had passed from bonfire to bonfire and now a crowd had gathered to wish them a safe journey with a final glass of wine. Although the ancient Englishman with the bizarre appearance merited perhaps the keener attention, all eyes were on Evgenia Ivanovna, who stood silent with the air of one who commits to memory a picture soon to be lost for ever.

As she looked at the friendly faces around her she realized quite sharply the change that had taken place in her. The warm expression in the eyes of these people of modest pride and hospitality freely given, of everyday care and even tragedy – all this had no longer anything to do with her. And she realized it not with the feeling of relief she had expected but with a stinging, guilty anxiety and a sense of irreparable loss. She was freed now from the sorrow of her native land, from all the difficulties it faced and would continue to face for many years from the ordeals and heartbreaks and everything that united these simple people in a common bitter bondage. She had only to stretch out her hand to touch them, but the sea already separated them from Evgenia Ivanovna, and when she smiled at them shyly from a distance, they responded with a friendly but cold restraint because to part with a foreigner in the old, familiar way was no longer polite or appropriate.

Mr Pickering began to thank the organizers of the feast and asked if they might ever have the chance of coming to England? No, was the reply, at present these opportunities did not seem to come their way.

'Live well, so the fire of eternal thought may never be extinguished, like your excellent Kakhetinian wine,' the Englishman said in farewell, almost without an accent.

'Dig into the past in such a way,' the natives replied with the same sincerity, 'that you will learn to make the future most honest and more beautiful.'

'Mshvidobit' . . . with an unexpected effort Mr Pickering managed the Georgian for 'au revoir'.

'Good-bye, genotsvali' the natives laughed good-naturedly, and one after another they gripped his shoulders in a gesture of farewell.

The driver came to ask if he should put the hood up on the Buick; the clouds over the mountains were grey and heavy. They stood for a moment, their arms lowered, leaving the end of the unspoken speeches to silence, then the driver pressed the horn and the crowd dispersed. Stratonov jumped into his seat as the car was moving. Only weeds growing along the side of the road flashed past them, bending under the wind. . . . Never in all her life possibly had Evgenia Ivanovna wanted so passionately to get anywhere as she wanted now to get to England, to enigmatic, foggy, England, where she was to die in the spring of the following year. It is to be presumed that the loneliness which then again befell Mr Pickering was what forced him to bury himself once and for all in excavations at Edessa which were his most successful and brought him universal recognition. . . . The British doctors explained his wife's death to him as the result of postnatal complications – their diagnosis would have been more accurate if, as well as the history of her illness, they had gleaned the little information about their patient which is given in this story.

Perhaps it is because the English never truly part with their country but are able miraculously to carry it with them wherever they go, that it is said they never sicken with longing for their native land. What they call nostalgia is little more than a passing discomfort due to change of climate, the break with the familiar background, the difficulties of communication in a foreign tongue. But when our own exiles, unspoilt by Western civilization, have attempted to bring away with them a handful of crisp Russian snow to countries with a more moderate climate, they have never been successful – the snow has unfailingly thawed.

Yet at this particular moment, Mrs Pickering felt unusually light-headed, almost weightless. Something forced her to turn round. . . . Through the dim oval window at the back of the car she could see the abandoned bonfire smouldering in the field. The wind combed from it handfuls of sparks that chased after them along the road. Then the Buick turned the corner by the olive grove, and thin scratches of rain appeared on the battered celluloid.

No Justification

to M. Gorky

No, I shall never welcome it;
    My just curse has a place.
I won't forgive nor will I rush
    Into the iron embrace.

Like all, I'll go, I'll die, I'll kill.
    Like all, I'll destroy me.
But I shall never stain my soul
    And justifier be.

In my last hours, in fire, in dark,
    Let my heart recall:
There's no reason for any war;
    There'll never be – at all.

And if it is God's handiwork,
    This road of bloodied clod . . .
My soul will wage war – against Him,
    Opposing even God.

ZINAIDA NIKOLAYEVNA HIPPIUS

The Death of Dolgushov

THE CURTAINS of battle were drawing towards the town. At noon Korochayev swept past us in his black cloak – Korochayev, Commander of the Fourth Division, fallen now into disfavour, battling on alone and seeking death. He yelled to me as he went:

'Our communications have been cut. Radziwillow and Brody are in flames! . . .'

And off he galloped, his cloak streaming behind him, all in black, with eyes like coals.

On the plain, flat as a board, the brigades were drawing up. The sun was veiled in dust, crimson. The wounded were taking a bite in the ditches. The nurses were lying in the grass, singing softly. Afonka's scouts were scurrying across the fields in search of bodies and equipment. Afonka passed within two paces of me and said, without so much as turning his head:

'We're getting a beating. That's for sure. There's talk about the Divisional Commander. He's going to be replaced. The troops don't trust him. . . .'

The Poles reached the woods a mile or so from us and set up their machine guns somewhere close by. Bullets began to whistle and shriek. Their wailing increased unbearably. Bullets struck the ground, burrowing into it, trembling with impatience. Vityagaichenko, the Regimental Commander, who had been snoring in the broiling sun, cried out in his sleep and woke up. He mounted his horse and set off towards the leading squadron. His face was crumpled, lined with red from the uncomfortable position in which he had been sleeping. His pockets were filled with plums.

'Son of a bitch,' he said angrily, spitting out a plumstone. 'This is a hell of a mess. Timoshka, out with the flag!'

'We're off, then?' asked Timoshka, taking the staff from his stirrup and unfurling the banner, on which was a star and a slogan about the Third International.

'We'll have a look over there,' said Vityagaichenko and suddenly bawled fiercely: 'Girls, get on your nags! Squadron Commanders, get your men together! . . .'

The buglers sounded the alarm. The squadrons formed a column. Then out of a ditch came a wounded man, covering his face with his hand.

'Taras Grigoryevich,' he said to Vityagaichenko, 'I've been picked as delegate. It looks to us as if we're going to get left behind. . . .'

'You'll manage . . .' Vityagaichenko muttered, rearing his mount on its hind legs.

'We've got a sort of idea, Taras Grigoryevich, that we won't,' the wounded man called after him.

'Stop moaning,' Vityagaichenko turned about, 'you know I won't leave you.' Then he ordered the men to be ready.

Immediately the tremulous, old-womanish voice of my friend Afonka Bida was heard.

'Don't be in too much of a hurry, Taras Grigoryevich. He's three or four miles from here. How can we fight if our horses are tired? . . . There's nothing to be gained – you'll get where you're going. . . .'

'Walking pace!', commanded Vityagaichenko without even a glance.

The regiment moved off.

'If what they reckon about the Divisional Commander is right,' Afonka whispered, hanging back, 'and he's replaced, then you'd better get ready for trouble. That's all there is to it.'

Tears spilled from Afonka's eyes. I stared at him in amazement. He spun round, clutched his cap, snorted, whooped and galloped off.

As for Grishchuk with his silly little gun-carriage, and me –

we stayed behind alone and wandered about till the evening be-tween walls of fire. The divisional headquarters had disappeared. Other units wouldn't take us. The regiments fought their way into Brody and were dislodged again by a counter-attack. We went up to the town cemetery. From behind the graves a Polish scout suddenly appeared, grabbed his rifle and started firing at us. Grishchuk turned about. All four wheels of his gun-carriage screeched.

'Grishchuk!' I shouted above the screeching and the wind.

'Some lark!' he answered mournfully.

'We're finished,' I exclaimed, suddenly seized by a mortal frenzy, 'we're finished, old man!'

'What's the point of women slaving away' he replied even more sadly, 'what's the point of betrothals and marriages? Why do chaps make merry at wedding feasts? . . .'

A red trail lit up the sky and was extinguished again. The Milky Way came into view amongst the stars.

'It makes me laugh,' Grishchuk said in an anguished voice, pointing with his whip at a man sitting by the roadside, 'it makes me laugh that women slave away, and. . . .'

The man sitting by the roadside was Dolgushov, our signaller. With legs flung wide he stared at us dully.

'Look at me,' Dolgushov said when we got to him, 'I'm a dead man. See?'

'I see,' Grishchuk replied, bringing his horse to a halt.

'You'd better use up a bullet on me,' Dolgushov said.

He was leaning against a tree, with his boots sticking out, wide apart. Without taking his eyes off me, he carefully pulled his shirt aside. His belly was torn apart, and his intestines were spilled out over his knees. I could see his heart beating.

'If the Polak finds me like this, he'll have some fun. Here's my documents. Write to my mother, tell her what happened, and how. . . .'

'I can't,' I said, spurring my horse.

Dolgushov spread out his blueing palms on the ground and looked at them distrustfully.

'So you're running away?' he mumbled, sliding down on the ground. 'You're running away, swine. . . .'

Sweat trickled down my body. Machine guns were rapping out faster and faster, with hysterical insistence. Framed in the nimbus of sunset, Afonka Bida came racing up to us.

'We're giving them a bit of a beating!' he shouted gaily. 'And what's going on here, then?'

I pointed to Dolgushov and rode away a little.

They talked for a moment – I didn't hear what they said. Dolgushov reached out his pay-book to the platoon commander. Afonka tucked it in his boot and shot Dolgushov through the mouth.

'Afonka,' I said with a wry smile, riding up to the Cossack, 'I just couldn't do it.'

'Go away!' he said, turning pale. 'or I'll kill you! You four-eyes have about as much pity for us as a cat has for a mouse. . .'

He cocked his rifle.

I set off at walking pace, not looking round, feeling the chill of death on my spine.

'Hey!' Grishchuk yelled behind Afonka, 'don't be so stupid!' He grabbed Afonka's arm.

'Breed of a milksop!' Afonka shouted. 'He won't get away from me! . . .'

Grishchuk caught up with me at the bend in the road. Afonka did not appear. He had gone off in the other direction.

'You see how it is,' I said. 'Today I've lost Afonka, the first friend I ever had. . . .'

Grishchuk took a shrivelled apple out of his driving seat.

'Eat this,' he said to me. 'Go on, eat it. Please. . . .'

ISAAC BABEL

'The worm of doubt . . .'

THE WORM of doubt has a nest in my soul,
But I am not ashamed of this. No fool,
A worm always likes mushrooms, good and whole;
He does not touch a sickening toadstool.

Zakhar the Pouch

MY FRIENDS, you would like me to tell you something about my cycling expeditions this summer? Very well, if it's not too dull, let me tell you about the battlefield of Kulikóvo.

We'd been aiming for it for a long time, but somehow none of the roads seemed to lead us there. There are no painted wooden shields to beckon you on, you know, and no signposts; and you won't find it marked on by any means every map, even though this fourteenth century battle gained more for the Russians, both materially and psychologically, than the nineteenth century battle of Borodinó. In five hundred years there was only one such battle, for the Russians and for the whole of Europe. It was a clash not of princedoms nor of national armies, but of continents.

Perhaps we hadn't picked a very wise route – from Epifániya via Kazánovka and Monastyrshchina. It was only because there hadn't yet been any rains that we were able to get through in the saddle instead of having to drag our bicycles by the handlebars. We crossed the Don – still low at this time – and the Nepryádva by wheeling our *vélos* across little foot-bridges, two planks wide.

From the top of a hill we'd caught sight much earlier of a sort of needle reaching up into the sky from another broad hilltop. But when we'd gone down into the valley we'd lost it again. Then we began again to labour upward, and again the grey needle appeared, clearer now, and alongside it had come into view what looked like a church. But it was a strange, unreal sort of structure such as one might dream of in a fairy tale. The cupolas seemed to be pierced through, transparent, and in the warm air currents of a hot August day they rippled and shimmered, one moment visible, the next moment gone.

It was a good thing we drank our fill at the well in the valley and filled our flasks – we were glad of this later. But the villager who handed round the pail looked at us as though we were daft when we asked him:

'Where's Kulikóvo field?'

'Not Kulikóvo,' he said, 'Kuléekovo. Kuléekovka village is right next to the field, but Kulikóvka's a long way in the other direction, on the Don.'

When we left him we set off along out of the way tracks, and until we arrived at the monument – a distance of several kilometres – we didn't meet a single soul. It was simply chance, but we didn't meet a soul. There was a reaper tractor weaving about in a field on one side, and people had been here and would be here again, for as far as eye could see the whole area was cultivated. There was buckwheat, beet, clover, oats, rye, peas already ripening (and we ate some of the young peas, straight from the pod), but on this day there was simply no one about and it was like going through a hushed, hallowed, sacred place. Our thoughts turned very easily to those red-haired warriors, to the nine out of every ten that were lying here, a yard or so down in the accumulated soil, dissolved to their very bones in the earth, that ancient Russia might shake off the pagan yoke.

This whole broad, gentle rise up to the Mamai heights can scarcely have changed in outline even in six centuries, except that it is not so wooded now. It was somewhere just here, within the eye's compass of this spot, that on the evening of 7th September and throughout that night almost a quarter of a million Russians – more than two hundred thousand – had come across the Don and deployed to feed their horses (though more were on foot than on horse), to sharpen their swords to a fine edge, summon their courage, pray and wonder about the morrow. In those times our people numbered but a seventh of what it does today, and such a force – two hundred thousand! – was beyond imagining.

Of each ten of those warriors, nine had awaited their last morning.

It was from no good cause that our men had crossed the Don, for who would willingly draw up for battle with a river cutting off his retreat? The historical truth is bitter, but we should tell it rather than hide it away. It was not only Circassians and Genoese that Mamai had brought with him, and the Lithuanians were not his only allies. Oleg, Prince of Ryazan, was also in league with him. (But we ought to understand Oleg, too. This was his only way of saving from the Tatars his own lands, which were lying in their path. They had scorched them for him seven years earlier, and three years earlier and two years earlier.) So the Russians crossed the Don to protect their rear from their own kinsfolk, the people of Ryazan, so that their own orthodox brethren might not strike at them.

The needle loomed before us, though it was no longer a needle but a stately tower, quite unlike any other. It was not easy to approach it; the cart tracks had ended, petering into cultivated land. We led our bicycles along the strips between plots until at last, out of the ground, beginning from nowhere, a roadway began to appear, overgrown, grass-covered, neglected, and nearer to the monument it became quite plain and even had ditches.

The cultivated land came to an end, and at the top of the hill began the reserved area, a section of bare, uncultivated field grown over not with feather-grass but with coarser growths. What better way to honour this ancient spot! Just breathe in the wild air and look about you, and see! Dawn, with Telebey and Peresvet locked in combat, the banners drawn up in opposing ranks, the Mongol horsemen loosing their arrows, whirling their spears and hurling themselves forward with frenzied faces to trample the Russian foot-soldiers, ripping out the kernel of the

Russians and pursuing us back whence we came, to where the milk white mist has risen in a cloud from the Nepryadva and the Don. And we fall like mown grass and perish beneath the hoofs.

Here at the heart of the savage battle – if the spot was correctly chosen – had been built the monument and the church with the unearthly cupolas that had puzzled us from a distance. The puzzle was easily solved. For their private uses, the local people had removed the tiles from all five cupolas, leaving them transparent. They retained their delicate form intact, but sketched only in outline, so that from far off they had seemed a mirage.

The monument, on the other hand, was amazing even from close by. Until one could go up and touch it, it was difficult to see how it was made. It was erected in the last century, more than a hundred years ago, but the idea of casting a tower in metal is completely modern, except that nowadays we shouldn't use iron. It had two plinths, one on top of the other, and a twelve-sided column, gradually becoming round, overlaid at first with rings of cast iron shields, swords, helmets and inscriptions in Old Slavonic. Then it stretched upward like a tube in four sections, each cast like closely packed organ pipes, and was crowned with a notched cap and, on the very top, a gilded cross over a crescent moon. All this reached a height of about thirty metres, made of figured plates held together internally with bolts in such a way that not a bolt or aperture was anywhere visible, so that it looked as if the entire monument had been cast in one piece, except that time – or rather grandsons and great-grandsons – had pierced it here and there.

After walking for some time through open fields, we approached the spot thinking to find it deserted, not expecting to meet anyone. As we walked we had pondered, why should this be so? Wasn't this where the fate of Russia had been decided? Hadn't the whole course of her history been changed at this spot? It had not always been through Smolensk and Kiev that our enemies had swarmed. . . . But here it was, unwanted, unknown to anyone.

How glad we were to find ourselves mistaken! First, not far from the monument, we came upon a grey-haired old man and two youngsters. They had thrown off their rucksacks and were stretched out on the grass, writing something in a large book, about the size of a class-register. We went up to them and learned that he was a teacher of literature, the boys he had picked up somewhere near by, and the book was no more nor less than a visitors' book. But there was no museum; who could be looking after it in the middle of nowhere?

Then a great shadow cut us off from the sun. We turned about – it was the Keeper of Kulikóvo Field – the man to whom it had befallen to be the guardian of our glory.

Bother, we had no time to adjust the focus! And you can't take snapshots against the sun. But in any case the Keeper would not have let us take him (he knew his worth, and not once throughout the day would he pose for us). But to describe him for you . . . him first? or his bag? He was carrying in his hands a simple, peasant bag, half-full and obviously not very heavy, because he never grew tired from carrying it.

The Keeper was a tough looking man, rather like a bandit in appearance. His arms and legs were immensely strong, his shirt all unbuttoned, his cap at a careless angle. His red hair had forced its way from under his cap, and he hadn't shaved that week, nor the week before, but there was a fresh red scratch across his entire cheek.

'Ah!' he greeted us in disapproval, hanging, as it were, above us. 'So you've arrived. How did you get here?'

He seemed indignant, as though there were a fence all round and we had crawled in through a hole. We nodded our heads towards our bicycles, leaning against some bushes. He was holding his bag as though about to board a train, and from the way he looked at us he was going to ask us at any moment for our passports. His face was thin and wedge-shaped, indecisive.

'I'm warning you,' he said. 'Don't damage the plants. With those bicycles, I mean.'

From this we understood that here, in Kulikóvo Field, people don't walk around any old how.

The Keeper was wearing an unbuttoned jacket with long skirts, capacious, like a sailor's coat, with patches here and there. It was a fantastic colour – grey cum brown cum raspberry. A star gleamed on the lapel. At first we thought it was a medal. But no! it was the star shaped badge of the October infants organization, with a portrait of Lenin in a circle inside it. Beneath his jacket he wore a long blue shirt with white stripes, the sort that could only have been made for him in the country, and around his waist was an army belt with a five-pointed star. His third-hand, diagonal-weave officer's trousers were tucked into oilskin boots, already worn at the tops.

'Well,' he asked the teacher less harshly, 'you still writing?'

'We'll be through in just a moment, Zakhar Dmitrich,' the latter said firmly.

'What about you?' (sternly again now). 'Are you going to write something?'

'Later.' And to divert his insistence, we added hastily. 'When was this monument put up, then? D'you know?'

'What!' he exclaimed indignantly, even choking and coughing with pique. 'What d'you think I'm here for?'

Then carefully putting down his bag (it clinked as if there were bottles in it), he took a document out of his pocket and unrolled it. It was a page out of an exercise book on which, in capital letters spilling over the lines, was written the dedication to Dmitry of the Don and the date of the erection of the monument – 1848.

'What's that, then?'

'This, my friends . . .' Zakhar Dmitrich sighed, naïvely displaying that he was by no means as tough as he had at first made out. 'You see, I copied this down from the plaque, because everyone wants to know when the monument was put up. I'll show where the plaque used to be, if you like.'

'What has happened to the plaque?'

'Some devil from our village pinched it and we can't do anything about it.'

'Do you know who it was?'

'Of course I know. I've got some of the letters back from him – I managed that much – but he's still got the rest. If only I had all the letters, I'd fix them up here.'

'Why did he steal the plaque?'

'He uses it for something at home.'

'But can't you take it from him?'

'Ah-ha!' Zakhar tossed his head at the silly question. 'That's just the point! I've got no authority! They won't even give me a rifle, though what I need here's an automatic.'

Looking at his scarred cheek we thought to ourselves it was just as well he *hadn't* been given a rifle!

At this moment the teacher finished writing in the visitors' book and returned it. We thought Zakhar Dmitrich would tuck it under his arm or put it in his bag. But no! – we were wrong. He pulled aside the skirt of his rather smelly jacket and there, sewn in the lining, we saw what was not exactly a pocket, not exactly a bag – more precisely a pouch made from sackcloth – exactly the size of the visitor's book, so that this fitted snugly inside it. On the pouch there was also a little slot for the blunt, indelible pencil that he also kept for visitors to use.

Having made sure that we were suitably impressed, Zakhar picked up his bag (yes, it still clinked of glass) and with his long-legged raking stride, his shoulders hunched forward, he walked off to one side under the shelter of some bushes. The brigand-like aggression with which he had addressed us when we arrived had left him now. He sat down, hunched his shoulders even closer, lit a cigarette, and smoked with an air of inconsolable grief and bereavement, as though all those that had perished here had been his brothers, his brothers-in-law, his sons, and he knew not how to go on living without them.

We decided to pass the rest of the day here and to stay for the night, to see what night at Kulikóvo – celebrated in verse by Blok – was really like. In a leisurely fashion we went up to the monument, examined the empty shell of the church or wandered about the field, trying to imagine where the combatants had stood on 8th September; or we clambered over the smooth, cast-iron surface of the monument.

There had certainly been people here before us, yes indeed! The devils hadn't lacked the energy to chisel away at the iron, or scratch it with nails; and the weaker ones had scrawled in charcoal on the walls of the church: 'Maria Poluneyeva's husband and Nikolai Lazarev were here from 8.V.50 to 24.V.' 'Delegates of the Regional Conferences were here. . . .'; 'Workers of the Kimov Regional Transport Committee were here ... 23.VI.52'; '. . . were here'; '. . . were here'.

Three young workers from Novomoskovsk arrived on motor-cycles. They jumped lightly up on to the monument and began examining it, slapping its grey-black body affectionately, marvelling how well it had been put together and explaining this to us. Then from the upper plinth we told them all we knew about the battle.

Though in fact who really knows where and how it all happened? According to the ancient chronicles, the Mongol-Tatar horsemen hacked through our foot-soldiers, thinning the ranks and chasing us back to the crossings on the Don, which flowed here in a bend that denied us defence from Oleg and threatened our doom. Dmitry of the Don might still have got his name, but for precisely the opposite reason! But no doubt he had calculated it all and was holding back in a way that not every great prince could do. Beneath his banner he left a Boyar in full regalia, while he himself fought like a simple warrior. People saw him engaging four Tatars at once. But even the great prince's standard fell and Dmitry, with his armour pierced, hardly managed to crawl into the trees, and we were being trampled and pursued. Then it was that from a plantation in the rear of the Tatars, raging now too far, came the attack from another Dmitry – the Muscovite leader, Volynsky-Bobrok. He drove the Tatars scurrying before him, advancing and then wheeling sharply to strike towards the Nepryadva. And from that moment the Russians took renewed heart. Rising out of the ground, they came back like a solid wall against the Tatars, and chased the entire command – including Mamai himself – for ten miles, across the river Ptan' and all the way to Krasivaya Mech'. (Here legend contradicts legend. One old man from the next village of Ivanovka has his own version. The mist, he says, would not disperse, and in it Mamai mistook an oakwood on his flank for a Russian army and took fright. 'Great is the God of the Christian peasants' he cried, and fled.)

For eight days after the battle the Russians sorted and buried the dead.

'They didn't gather one of them, they left him here!' joked the carpenter from Novomoskovsk in mock reproach.

We turned, and it was impossible not to burst out laughing. Yes! One prostrate warrior still lay there, not far from the monument. He lay face down on mother earth, his bold head laid low, his youthful arms and legs flung yards apart. He had no shield, no sword; and in place of a helmet – a bedraggled cap and by his hand, his bag. (But it was noticeable that the skirt of his jacket, with the pouch in which he kept the visitors' book, was not crushed beneath his stomach but stretched out alongside him on the grass.) And provided only that he wasn't lying like that from drunkenness, but was asleep or deep in thought, then the way his arms and legs were outstretched expressed real grief. It went very well with the Field. They ought to make a cast-iron figure like that and leave it there.

But for a bold warrior, Zakhar was, despite his height, a little flabby.

'He doesn't want to work on the farm, so he's fixed himself up with a nice little job, getting sunburnt,' said another of the youngsters in sudden annoyance.

What particularly displeased us was the way Zakhar pounced on newcomers, especially those from whose appearance he expected trouble. Several more arrived during the day, and at the sound of an engine he would jump to his feet, shake himself and immediately descend menacingly on them as though they, and not he, were responsible for the monument. He waxed more indignant about the vandalism than they did, and before they did. His indignation was so fierce that we could hardly believe his breast capable of accommodating it.

'What did you think?' with arms waving he accosted four visitors in a Zaporozhets car. 'I'll wait a bit, wait a bit, then I'll go right over the heads of the district office of culture!' (His legs were quite long enough for him to be able to do this.) 'I'll take my holiday and go to Moscow, right to Furtseva! I'll tell her everything!'

But as soon as he saw that the visitors had taken fright and had no intention of opposing him, he would pick up his bag (with an important air, like the head of a department picking up his briefcase) and go off to one side to hunch himself up and light a cigarette.

We came upon Zakhar several times during the day as we were wandering here and there. Noticing that as he walked he trod more heavily on one foot than on the other, we asked him why this was.

'A souvenir of the front!' he replied proudly, but again we didn't believe him. He was laying it on too thick now, the rascal.

Our flasks were sucked dry, so we went up to Zakhar to find out where we could get some water. Wa-a-t-e-r? That was just it, he explained, there was no well, they wouldn't give any money to dig one, and in all that famous field the only water to be drunk was from puddles. For a well, one had to go to the village.

Regarding us now as old acquaintances he no longer jumped to his feet at our approach.

At one time we started swearing about the graffiti, carved or scratched. Zakhar protested.

'You just look! What years were they? Find a fresh one, and you can drag me into it. The vandals did all that before my time. Just let them try it now! Well, maybe some swine has managed to hide himself in the church and write something, but I've only got one pair of legs!'

The church – named after Sergey of Radonezh, who had united the Russian forces for the battle, and some time after it reconciled Dmitry of the Don and Oleg of Ryazan – had been constructed like a true fortress – a closely packed corpus of solid slabs, the cut-off pyramid of the church proper, a transverse structure with a watchtower and two round fortress towers. The few windows were like slits.

Not only had everything been torn out from inside but even the floor had gone, leaving bare sand. We questioned Zakhar about this.

'Aha! So now you're on the track!' he rejoiced at our distress. 'That's because our people from Kuléekovo tore all the flag-stones up during the war to pave their own yards so they wouldn't be muddy. I've made a note how many each one's got. . . . And the front came through here, too, and people weren't idle. . . . Even before our own men got here all the boards from the screen had been used to line dugouts or burnt for firewood.'

Growing hourly more used to us, Zakhar was no longer so jealous of the contents of his bag. He either put things in or took things out until gradually we built up a picture of what it contained. There were empty bottles (twelve kopeks each) and glass jars (five kopeks) that he had collected from the bushes where visitors had left them. Then there was a bottle of water – since even for him there was no other drinking water for the entire day. And there were two loaves of rye bread. From time to time he would break off a piece and chew it just as it was.

'People are crowding in all day. No time to go down the village for a meal.'

Perhaps on other days he had the eternal quarter litre of vodka or a tin of preserved fish, and this was why he carted the bag around with him and was afraid to put it down. On this day, when the sun was already going down, a friend of his came up on a motor-cycle. They sat for an hour and a half in the bushes, then the friend went away and Zakhar came out without his bag, speaking more loudly and waving his arms wider. When he saw me writing something he said warningly:

'The place *is* looked after! It *is*! In '57 they passed a decree about erecting something here. D'you see those posts dug in around the monument? They date from then. They were cast in Tula. And there were supposed to be chains running from post to post, but the chains were never brought. Then they appointed me to watch over it. If it weren't for me, it would all have been smashed to smithereens!'

'How much do you get paid, Zakhar Dmitrich?'

He gave a sigh like a smith's bellows, but without a word. Then he hunched himself up and said quietly:

'Twenty-seven rubles.'

'How is that possible? The minimum wage is thirty.'

'Well, it is possible. . . . And no days off. From morning to night, without a break. And at night, too.'

Ah, now you've overdone it, Zakhar!

'Why at night, too?'

'What d'you mean?' He was offended now. 'D'you think I can just leave everything? I've got to be on guard at night, too, see. If a car comes, I take the number down.'

'What d'you want the number for, then?'

'Well, they won't give me a rifle. Reckon I'd shoot them visitors! So all I can do is take down the number. What if they do some damage?'

'But to whom d'you give the number then?'

'Nobody, of course. I keep it. . . . They've built a guest house now. Have you seen it? I've got to guard that, too.'

We'd seen this hut of course. It was one-storied, with several rooms, and was nearly completed but all locked up. The windows had been put in and some of the panes were already broken. The floors were covered, but the plastering wasn't finished.

'Will you let us spend the night in there?' (Towards sunset a chill had arisen, and the night promised to be severe.)

'In the guest house? Certainly not.'

'Well, who is it for, then?'

'Certainly not! I haven't even got the key. So don't ask me. You can spend the night in my little shack.'

His little shack, leaning to one side, was about big enough for a half-dozen sheep. We stooped down and peered inside. The bedding was crushed, worn-out hay, and on the floor there was a pot of half-eaten stew, a few empty bottles and a completely dried up piece of bread. But there was room enough for our bicycles and for us to lie down, leaving space for its owner to stretch out, too.

But he wasn't fool enough to stay there for the night.

'I'm going to have some supper. At home, in Kuléekovka, I'll grab something hot. You shut the door on the hook.'

'Give us a knock when you get back!' we said, laughing at him.

'Right.'

Zakhar the Pouch pulled back the other skirt of his fantastic jacket – not the one where the visitors' book was kept – and there we saw two loops sewn on it. Then from his fabulous bag he took out an axe with a shortened handle and fastened it firmly in the loops.

'There,' he said gloomily, 'that's all I've got. They won't allow me anything else.'

He said this with real foreboding, as though he thought that any night a horde of Mongols would gallop up to overturn the monument, and no one would be there to meet them except him, armed only with his little axe. He said it in such a way that we even shuddered in the dusk. Perhaps he was not a rogue at all? Perhaps he really believed that if it weren't for his night vigil the Field would be destroyed?

But then, faint from drinking and a day of noisiness and running about, stooped and slightly limping, Zakhar hurried off to the village, and again we laughed at him.

As we had wished, we were left alone on Kulikóvo Field. Night came, with a full moon. The tower of the monument and the fortress-church stood out like dark barriers against it. The dim, distant lights of Kuléekovo and Ivanovka were drowned in the moonlight. Not a single aircraft passed over. Not a single car engine droned past. Not a single train rattled by from any direction. The edges of the cultivated fields were not visible in the light of the moon. This land, this grass, this moon, this silence were the same as in 1380. On this hallowed ground the centuries stood still, and as we wandered over the darkened field we could envisage everything just as it had been; the camp fires and the dark herds of horses, and away towards the Nepryadva, the sound of Blok's swans.

We wanted to grasp the real meaning of the battle of Kulikóvo in all its fullness and irrevocability, shrugging off the strident embellishments of the chroniclers; to comprehend that all had not taken place so instantly, so simply; that history moved in loops, doubling back on itself and strangling. That after this dearly-won victory the Russian land had been impoverished of warriors. That Mamai had straightaway been replaced by

Tokhtamysh; that only two years after Kulikóvo, Tokhtamysh had moved on Moscow; Dmitry of the Don had fled to Kostroma and Tokhtamysh had again sacked both Ryazan and Moscow, taking the Kremlin by a trick, plundering, burning, beheading and once again leading off prisoners in bondage to the Horde.

The centuries pass and the loops of History are smoothed away in the distant view, so that she seems like the extended tape of the topographer.

The night became bitterly cold, and when we shut ourselves up in the little shack, we slept soundly. We had decided to leave very early, and as soon as it began to grow light we wheeled out our bicycles and, with teeth chattering, began to load them.

The grass was white with frost and from the direction of Kuléekovka, down below us, ropes of mist were threading across the stook-covered fields.

We had hardly left the wall of the shack to get into the saddle and move off when out of one of the stooks came a loud, angry barking and a shaggy-jowled grey dog came bounding at us. As it ran towards us the stook disintegrated behind it. Awoken by the barking, a lanky figure rose from out of it, called to the dog and began shaking itself free of straw. It was light enough now for us to recognize our own Zakhar the Pouch, dressed in some sort of coat with short sleeves.

He had spent the night in the stook in that fierce cold! Why? what concern or sense of duty had compelled him to?

Immediately we shed all feelings of mockery and condescension that we had harboured towards him the day before. As he rose out of the stook at that frosty dawn he was no longer simply the Keeper – he was the Spirit of Kulikóvo Field, a guardian faun that never left it.

He came towards us, still shaking himself and rubbing his hands together, and from beneath his cap, tipped on to his forehead, he looked like an old, true friend.

'But why didn't you knock, Zakhar Dmitrich?'

'Didn't want to bother you.' He shrugged his chilled shoulders, yawning. He was covered with corn husks. He unbuttoned his coat to shake himself, and we saw the visitors' book safely in its place, plus the little axe, all that he was allowed.

The grey dog stood alongside him, its teeth bared.

We said goodbye warmly. We had already begun to pedal off, and he was standing there, when he raised a long arm and called to us in reassurance.

'No-o! No-o, I won't leave it like this! I'll go right up to Furtseva! To Furtseva!'

All this was some two years ago. Perhaps things are better ordered now and better cared for. This isn't a pamphlet written when opportunity was ripe, you know: I was simply reminded of our eternal Field and of its Keeper, its red-haired spirit.

But now that I am reminded – for us Russians to neglect that spot would not be very wise.

To be Famous is Unbecoming

To be famous is unbecoming –
This does not raise one to the heights.
One should not start an archive, trembling
Over the manuscript's delights.

Creation's aim is a self-giving –
Not success with applause. Not quips
Nor big to-do which (Shame!) mean nothing:
Legend on everybody's lips.

One should live with no pretensions,
So one attracts – in the long run –
To oneself the love of expanses
And hears the future calling one.

And one should leave gaps – not on paper –
But in one's destiny instead,
And mark the margins with the places
And parts where a whole life is read.

And to submerge into the unknown
And hide one's steps neath covering –
As in a fog a space is hidden
Till one cannot see anything.

And all the live footsteps of others,
Inch after inch, will walk your street.
But you yourself should not distinguish
A victory from a defeat.

And you must not – by one small portion
Even – renounce your face, my friend.
But be alive, that's all that matters,
Alive and living – to the end.

BORIS LEONIDOVICH PASTERNAK

A Rainy Dawn

THE STEAMER arrived in Navolki at night. Major Kuzmin came out on deck. Rain was drizzling down. The jetty was empty: just one solitary lantern glowed.

'Wonder where the town itself is?' thought Kuzmin. 'It's dark, it's raining: God knows what else!'

He went on, buttoning up his overcoat. A cold draught blew up the sleeves.

Kuzmin tracked down the mate and asked him whether the steamer would make a long stop in Navolki.

'Three hours,' answered the mate. He was watching the loading. 'Why? You're going on with us.'

'I have to deliver a letter. From someone I was in hospital with. To his wife. She's here, in Navolki.'

'Got a problem there,' the mate sighed. 'It's pitch black out there. Listen for the hooters or you'll get left behind.'

Kuzmin crossed over to the jetty and climbed slippery steps to the top of the steep bank. He could hear bushes rustling beneath the rain. Kuzmin stood still for a moment to accustom his eyes to the darkness; he caught sight of a wretched horse, bent from pulling a cab. The hood of the cab was pulled over. From under it issued the sound of snores.

'Hey, cabby,' Kuzmin called him loudly. 'Wake up for goodness' sake.'

The driver stirred, emerged, blew his nose, wiped it with the flap of his cloth coat, and only then did he ask, 'Ready to go?'

'Ready,' agreed Kuzmin.

'Where to?'

Kuzmin named the street.

'Long way.' The cabby sounded worried. 'Uphill. I couldn't take you for less than the price of a small bottle of vodka.'

He drew on the reins and clicked. The cab moved unwillingly forward.

'I suppose you're the only cabby in Navolki?' asked Kuzmin.

'There are two of us, old 'uns. The rest are fighting. Who is it you want to see?'

'Bashilova.'

'I know her.' The cabby turned round interested. 'Olga Andreyevna, the daughter of the doctor, Andrei Petrovitch. She arrived from Moscow last winter and took to living in her father's house. Andrei Petrovitch himself passed on two years ago, and their house. . . .'

The cab lurched, pitched into a rut, then bumped out again.

'You'd better watch the road,' advised Kuzmin. 'Don't keep turning round.'

'Watch the road indeed . . .' muttered the cabby. 'It's all very well getting scared in daylight. Not at night. You can't see the holes.'

The driver stopped talking. Kuzmin lit up a cigarette, and settled back in the cab. The rain drummed on the raised hood. Far away dogs were barking. He could smell fennel, damp fences, river dampness.

'Must be at least one o'clock,' thought Kuzmin. At that moment a bell struck once in some clock-tower.

'I could spend all my leave here,' thought Kuzmin. 'Everything would pass in a flash, all the misery after the wound. I could take a room in a little house with windows looking on to a garden. On a night like this I could open the window wide, lie there, wrap myself up, and listen to the rain beating on the burdocks.'

'You're not her husband, are you?' asked the cabby.

Kuzmin did not answer. The driver thought that the soldier had not heard his question, but decided not to ask again.

'Obviously is her husband:' the cabby considered the question, 'but people say she threw over her husband before the war. Still, they must be lying.'

'Hey, you devil!' he yelled and struck the scraggy horse with the reins. 'Silly old nanny of a horse!'

'Stupid of the steamer to wait and come at night,' thought Kuzmin. When he discovered that Kuzmin was passing through Navolki, why did Bashilov, his room-mate, ask him to hand the letter personally to his wife? 'I'll have to wake these people up and God knows what they'll think of that.'

Bashilov was a tall sneering officer. He liked talking and did so often. Before coming out with some cutting remark, he would laugh long and silently. Until his call-up Bashilov had been the assistant manager of a cinema. Every evening he would regale his room-mates with detailed descriptions of American films. The wounded used to love Bashilov's descriptions; they looked forward to them and marvelled at his memory. Bashilov was cutting, very stubborn and apt to deride anyone who tried to argue with him. But his derision was sly – he used veiled hints and jokes – after an hour or two the butt of his mockery would suddenly wake up to the fact that Bashilov had insulted him, and would think up a cutting answer. By then, of course, it was too late to be effective.

The day before Kuzmin left, Bashilov gave him the letter for his wife, and for the first time Kuzmin noticed a smile of embarrassment on his face. Later that night Kuzmin heard Bashilov tossing around in his bunk and blowing his nose.

'Maybe he's not such a cad,' thought Kuzmin. 'It sounds as if he's crying. That means he loves her; loves her very much.'

The whole of the next day Bashilov never left Kuzmin's side. He kept looking at him, and gave him an Italian officer's hip-flask. Then just before Kuzmin finally left, the two of them drank a bottle of wine, which Bashilov had kept on one side.

'Why do you look at me like that?' asked Kuzmin.

'You're a good man,' answered Bashilov. 'You could have been an artist, my dear major.'

'I'm a topographer,' said Kuzmin, 'and topography isn't a science, it's an art.'

'Why?'

'Tramps,' Kuzmin replied vaguely.

'Exiles, tramps and poets,' Bashilov declaimed mockingly, 'who yearn to be, but are unable to become anything.'

'Who's that from?'

'Voloshin. But that's beside the point. I'm looking at you because I envy you, and that's all there is to it.'

'Why do you envy me?'

Bashilov put down his glass, leaned back against his chair, and smiled. They were sitting at the end of the hospital corridor, by a little wicker table. Outside the window the young trees were leaning with the wind which rustled their leaves and whipped up the dust. A rain cloud drew over the town from behind the river.

'Why do I envy you?' Bashilov repeated the question and put his red hand on Kuzmin's. 'For everything. Even your hand. Not the left one; this right one.'

'I don't understand at all,' said Kuzmin and carefully drew his hand away. He disliked the touch of Bashilov's cold fingers, but since Bashilov had not noticed this, Kuzmin picked up the bottle and began to pour out the wine.

'So you don't understand,' Bashilov's answering tone was angry.

He was quiet for a moment, then looked up and began:

'If only we could change places! No, that's stupid. You'll be in Navolki in two days' time. You'll see Olga Andreyevna. She will squeeze your hand. And I envy you. Now do you understand?'

'Well, I don't know,' Kuzmin was embarrassed. 'You'll see your wife too.'

'She's not my wife,' Bashilov answered sharply. 'It would be best for you not to call her "Mrs."'

'I'm sorry,' muttered Kuzmin.

'She's not my wife!' Bashilov repeated this as sharply as before. 'She's everything. My whole life. But never mind.'

He stood up and shook Kuzmin's hand. 'Goodbye. Don't be angry with me. I'm no worse than any of the others.'

The cab made its way towards the dam. The darkness thickened. Rain rustled hollowly in the ancient white willows, and trickled down the leaves. The horse clopped along the wood paved track.

'It has been a long way,' sighed Kuzmin and turned to the cabby: 'Wait for me by the house. We'll go straight back to the jetty.'

'All right.' The cabby was only too ready to do so and thought to himself, 'No, can't be her husband, the husband would be bound to stay for at least a day, if not two. This one's a stranger.'

The road changed to cobblestones. The cab began to shake and tremble on its iron undercarriage. The cabby guided it to the side of the road. The wheels slipped softly over the grey sand. Kuzmin took to musing again.

So Bashilov envied him. Though it was certainly not real envy; Bashilov had not used the right word. On the contrary, after his talk with Bashilov by the hospital window Kuzmin had begun to envy him. 'That's not the right word either,' Kuzmin muttered to himself, feeling aggrieved. He was not envious. He simply regretted. Regretted that he had never known a love like Bashilov's. He had always been alone. Night-time. Rain shuffling through empty gardens. Some-one else's town, covered with fog from the meadows: 'That's life,' thought Kuzmin for some reason.

At first he would have liked to stay here. He liked small Russian towns, where, from a little back porch, you could see fields stretching along the river, wide open spaces, hay carts on ferries. Even he was surprised by this love of his. He had been born in the South, in a naval family. From his father he had inherited a weakness for prospecting and geographical maps, and wanderlust. Because of this he had become a topographer. Kuzmin considered this profession completely fortuitous, and thought that if he had been born in another age he would have been a hunter, a discoverer of new lands, an adventurer. He liked to think of himself like that, but it was not a true picture: his character showed nothing likely to make him that sort of person. Kuzmin was shy, and treated people gently. His thin grey hair betrayed his age, but no-one looking at this small slim officer would have put him at over thirty.

The cab eventually reached the darkened town. There was only one house lit up; it must have been a chemist's with its blue light glowing through the glass door. The road led up the hillside. The cabby got down to lighten the horse's load. Kuzmin also got down. He walked a little way behind the cab, and suddenly thought of all the strangeness of his life:

'Where am I?' he thought. 'Some town called Navolki, a backwater, and a horse's hooves making sparks fly. Somewhere along the way is an unknown woman. I must give her, in the middle of the night, an important and probably sad letter. Yet two months ago we were at the front: Poland, the Visla, silently stretching away. How strange it seems. Good too.'

The slope evened out. The cabby turned off into a side street. The clouds were parting here and there, and in the blackness overhead an odd star twinkled. It seemed to be lit up and then switched off.

The cab stopped by a house with a gabled roof.

'There you are,' said the cabby, 'there's a bell on the right of the porch.'

Kuzmin fumbled for the wooden bell handle, and pulled it, but no noise came, except the grating of a rusty wire.

'Pull harder,' came the cabby's advice. Kuzmin reached for the handle again. From the depths of the house came the muffled sound of a bell, but the house remained as quiet as before. Obviously no-one had woken up.

'Oh dear,' the cabby yawned, 'A night full of rain and a very deep sleep.'

Kuzmin waited, rang harder. He heard steps on wooden floorboards. Someone came to the door, stopped, listened, then grumpily asked:

'Who's there? What do you want?'

Kuzmin wanted to answer, but was interrupted by the cabby.

'Open up, Marfa,' he said, 'There's someone for Olga Andreyevna. From the front.'

'Who from the front?' the voice behind the door was still sour. 'We're not expecting anyone.'

'Expected or not, he's arrived.'

The door opened a crack. Kuzmin told the darkness who he was and why he had come.

'Goodness me,' the woman behind the door was startled. 'What a lot of trouble you've gone to. Just a minute while I unlock. Olga Andreyevna is asleep. Wait here and I'll wake her.'

The door opened and Kuzmin stepped into a dark corridor.

'Mind the steps,' warned the woman, who had already developed a different and more pleasant tone of voice. 'What a night, and you coming all this way! Careful you don't fall. I'll light a lamp right away; we don't keep a light on at night.'

She disappeared and Kuzmin waited in the passage. The rooms exuded a smell of tea and something rather weaker, but pleasant. A cat appeared in the passage, rubbed against Kuzmin's leg, miaowed, and went back into the dark room as if inviting him to follow it.

A weak light glimmered through the half-open door.

'Please come in,' said the woman.

Kuzmin went in. The woman bowed to him. She was a tall old woman with a swarthy face. Trying not to make too much noise Kuzmin took off his coat and cap and hung them on a peg by the door.

'Now don't look so worried; it doesn't matter that Olga Andreyevna had to be woken up,' the old woman smiled.

'Can you hear the hooters on the jetty from here?' Kuzmin asked in a whisper.

'Gracious me, yes. You can easily hear them. That means you've come off the steamer and have to get back. Just sit you down on the sofa there.'

The old woman went off. Kuzmin sat on the wooden-backed sofa, hesitated, fingered a cigarette, and then lit it. He felt disturbed and the unpleasantness of this feeling angered him. He felt as people always feel in a strange house at night, breaking in on someone else's life full of secrets and surmises. This life lies like a forgotten book on the table open at about page sixty-five. You begin to inspect that page and try to guess what the book is about, what it consists of. Could it be a Turgenev novel with one of his maidens trembling with love, and the sun sinking behind spreading lime trees? Or perhaps it is one of Katyush Maslovaya's bitter stories.

In actual fact an open book *was* lying on the table. Kuzmin stood up, leant over it and, keeping an ear on the hasty whispering outside the door and the rustling of a dress, read the words which he had long since forgotten:

> '*The impossible is possible,*
> *The distant way is easy,*
> *When the fleeting glance of a dear one*
> *Shines into the darkness from behind her shawl.*'

Kuzmin raised his eyes and had a look round. The small, low room reawakened his wish to stay in the town.

There is a special open-hearted cosiness which goes with such rooms, with the lamp in a frosted white shade hanging over the dining table, and the antlers over the picture of a dog by a sick

girl's bed. Such rooms call forth a smile: everything is so old-
fashioned, long forgotten.

Everything there, even the pink shell ashtray, spoke of a long,
steady life. Maybe it was the awareness of a steady life, which
Kuzmin had never known, that made him want to stay there, and
live like the inhabitants of this old house; live leisurely, alter-
nating work with rest, winter with spring, rainy with sunny days.
A desire to be absorbed in the flow of a life unclouded by emo-
tional upsets, where even old age does not frighten or torment,
neither do the summer evenings fading fast into the darkness of
night.

But amongst the old things there were others: a bunch of wild
flowers was standing on the table – camomile, lungwort, wild
rowan. The flowers must have been gathered some time ago.
There were scissors too lying on the table with the ends of the
flower stalks which they had cut off.

Beside them, the open book by Blok, 'The distant way is
easy.' On a blue plush photograph album on the piano lay a
woman's small, black hat. Far from being old, it was a very
fashionable hat, thrown carelessly on one side. On the table was
a watch attached to a nickel bracelet. It was ticking noiselessly
and gave the time as half past one. There is always a faint, sad
smell of perfume, especially this late at night.

One half of the window was open. Outside, behind the vase of
begonias, a wet lilac bush blinked in the uncertain light falling
on it through the window. A feeble drizzle whispered to itself in
the darkness, but heavy drops banged fiercely on the tin gutter-
ing.

Kuzmin listened to the banging of these drops. Thoughts of
the inevitability of every minute, which have worried generations of people, entered his head at that moment, in this strange
house, which he would leave in a few minutes never to return.

'Must be old age coming on,' thought Kuzmin and turned
around.

In the doorway stood a young woman in a black dress. She had obviously been in a hurry to get down to him; her hair was not done properly. One curl was falling on to her shoulder and the woman, staring fixedly at Kuzmin and smiling with embarrassment, found it and pinned it up with the hair at the nape of her neck.

Kuzmin bowed.

'I'm very sorry to have kept you waiting,' said the woman taking Kuzmin's hand.

'Are you Olga Andreyevna?'

'Yes.'

Kuzmin looked at this woman. He was surprised by her youth and by the light in her deep and slightly clouded eyes.

Kuzmin apologized for the trouble he was causing, took Bashilov's letter out of his tunic pocket and gave it to the woman. She took the letter, thanked him, and put it unread on the piano.

'Look at us, still standing,' she said. 'Do sit down, here, by the table – there's more light here.'

Kuzmin sat down at the table and asked her permission to smoke.

'Do please smoke,' said the woman. 'Perhaps I'll have one too.'

Kuzmin offered her a cigarette, and struck a match. As she inhaled, the match lit up her face, and her concentrated expression with its clean brow seemed familiar to Kuzmin.

Olga Andreyevna sat opposite Kuzmin. He was expecting to be questioned, but she was silently looking out of the window where the rain plashed monotonously down.

'Marfusha,' said Olga Andreyevna and turned towards the door, 'Would you bring the samovar.'

'No, don't bother,' Kuzmin was alarmed. 'I'm in a hurry. I have a cabby waiting outside. I just had to give you the letter and tell you how . . . your husband is.'

'What is there to tell?' replied Olga Andreyevna taking a

camomile from the bunch of flowers and pitilessly beginning to strip it of petals. 'He is alive, and I am glad.'

Kuzmin was silent.

'Do stay.' Olga Andreyevna spoke to him like an old friend. 'We'll hear the hooters. The steamer certainly won't go before dawn.'

'Why?'

'The river has more shoals here than lower down at Navolki,' said Marfa from the next room. 'It's dangerous crossing it at night so the captains wait till dawn.'

'It's quite right,' Olga Andreyevna assured him, 'and you can reach the jetty in quarter of an hour by foot, if you go across the municipal park. I'll show you the way. You can send off the cabby. Who brought you? Vasily?'

'I don't know his name.' Kuzmin smiled.

'It was Timofey who brought you,' came Marfa's voice from behind the door. They could hear her clanking the samovar's pipe. 'You can manage just a cup of tea. You're well out of the rain too, instead of getting soaked.'

Kuzmin agreed, went out to the gate, and paid the cabby. He lost no time in hurrying off beside his horse, leading it by the bridle.

When Kuzmin got back inside, the table was already laid. There were blue cups with gold rims, a jug of boiled milk, honey, and a half-drunk bottle of wine. Marfa brought in the samovar.

Olga Andreyevna apologized for the meagre food, and told him that she would be returning to Moscow, but meanwhile had a job in the town library at Navolki. Kuzmin was quite sure that she would ask about Bashilov sooner or later, but she did not. He had already guessed, while in hospital, that Bashilov had had some sort of quarrel with his wife. Now, after seeing her put the letter unopened on the piano, he was quite sure of this, felt that he was not doing his duty by Bashilov, and was overcome by guilt.

'She's obviously going to read the letter later,' he thought. One thing was clear though: this letter, which had meant so much to Bashilov, and on account of which Kuzmin had appeared in this house at this unearthly hour, was neither needed nor interesting here. So after all, Kuzmin had been no help to Bashilov; he had just put him in an unenviable position. As if she guessed his thoughts, Olga Andreyevna interrupted them.

'Don't be angry. There's a postal and a telegraph service. I don't know why he had to put you to all this trouble.'

'It's no trouble,' Kuzmin hastened to answer, and quietly added, 'On the contrary, it's very nice.'

'What's nice?'

Kuzmin blushed.

'What's nice?' Olga Andreyevna raised her voice to ask again, and stared straight at Kuzmin. She looked at him as if trying to guess what he was thinking, leaning forward and sternly waiting for an answer. But Kuzmin said nothing.

'What is it, what's nice?' Again she asked him.

'How can I tell you?' He answered pensively. 'This is a peculiar conversation. Everything we love in life happens only rarely. I don't know about other people, I'm judging by myself. The best things almost always pass. Do you understand?'

'Not really,' answered Olga Andreyevna and frowned.

'I don't know how to explain it,' said Kuzmin getting angry with himself. 'It's probably happened to you too. From a train window you suddenly catch sight of a clearing in a birch forest: you see how the sun lights up the autumn colours, and you desperately want to run out of the train and stand there in that clearing. But the train goes past it. You lean out of the window to where all those groves, meadows, horses and country roads are being carried away, and you hear a muffled ringing. You don't understand what it is. It might be the forest or the air. It might be telegraph wires humming, or it might be the rails singing under the train. It flashes by in a moment, and you will remember it all your life.'

Kuzmin stopped talking. Olga Andreyevna pushed a glass of wine over to him.

'Drink it. It's Riesling.'

'All my life,' said Kuzmin and coloured as he always did when it came to talking about himself, 'I have waited for just such unexpected and simple things. When I found them, I was happy. It happened not long ago.'

'And now too?' asked Olga Andreyevna.

'Yes.'

Olga Andreyevna looked down.

'Why?' she asked.

'I'm not sure exactly. I just feel very aware of it. I was wounded in Visla and lying in the hospital. Everyone was getting letters, but not me. There was simply no-one to write to me. Like everyone else probably, I lay there and considered what would happen to me after the war. I was definitely going to be happy and make a new start. Then I got better and they decided to send me off to convalesce. They recommended a town.'

'Which one?' asked Olga Andreyevna.

Kuzmin told her. Olga Andreyevna said nothing.

'I got on to the steamer,' continued Kuzmin, 'villages on the banks, jetties, and for me a definite feeling of solitude. Please don't think I'm complaining; there's a lot to be said for solitude. Then Navolki. I was frightened of missing it. I came out on deck in the depths of the night, and thought how strange it was that this darkness was enveloping all the huge mass of Russia, and that thousands of people were sleeping calmly under this rain-filled sky. And at that moment their life stays still. Then day will start to pull and weave – how shall I put it? – the threads of all our fates. Both yours and mine. Then I came up here by cab, and all the time I wondered what sort of person I was going to meet.'

'And why are you so happy now?' asked Olga Andreyevna.

'Because. . . .' Kuzmin suddenly thought, 'Life's good.' He was quiet.

'What are you thinking? Tell me.'

'About what? I was all mixed up. I've talked too much.'

'About everything,' answered Olga Andreyevna as if she had not heard his last remark. 'About whatever you like,' she added, 'although all this is rather strange.'

She stood up, went over to the window and drew back the curtains. The rain was still coming down.

'What's strange?' asked Kuzmin.

'All this rain!' said Olga Andreyevna and turned round. 'Here's you a single man. And I too am alone. Meeting you in this way. All this conversation in the night. Surely it's all strange?'

Kuzmin was silent and embarrassed. Olga Andreyevna went up to the calendar and tore off a sheet.

'June 12th. I keep forgetting how many days there are in a year.'

'Three hundred and sixty-five.'

'I'm twenty-eight. How many days would that be?'

Kuzmin considered, then smiled, 'About ten thousand.'

'Right. If we say childhood took five thousand days, then it means I've expected something wonderful to happen five thousand times. I've waited, like all of us wait, every single day. But nobody could tell me, or even hazard a guess, which of these days would finally be the most unforgettable.'

She raised shining eyes to Kuzmin and asked, 'I'm talking nonsense, aren't I?'

Kuzmin wanted to tell her that it was far from nonsense, but in the grey twilight through the window the steamer hooted somewhere at the foot of the hill.

'Well there you are,' Olga Andreyevna sounded relieved, 'there's your hooter.'

Kuzmin stood up. Olga Andreyevna did not move.

'Wait,' she said quietly. 'Let's sit a while before we leave, like they did in the olden days.'

Kuzmin sat down again. Olga Andreyevna also sat, thinking; she even turned away from Kuzmin. As he watched her high shoulders, her heavy hair fastened in a bun at the nape of her neck, and the neck's pure curve, Kuzmin thought that if it was not for Bashilov he would not have left this little town, he would have stayed here until his leave ended, and lived, excited and knowing that beside him lived this precious, and at the moment very sad woman, longing and waiting for her most unforgettable day.

Olga Andreyevna got up. In the small entrance hall Kuzmin helped her on with her coat. She wrapped a shawl round her head.

They left the house and walked silently along the dark street.

'It'll soon be dawn,' said Olga Andreyevna.

Over the other side of the river shone a watery sky. Kuzmin noticed that Olga Andreyevna was shivering.

'Are you cold?' He was concerned. 'Don't worry about showing me the way. I can find it by myself.'

'It's no bother,' Olga Andreyevna answered shortly.

The rain had stopped, but drops still plashed from the roofs on to the boarded pavement.

The end of the street led into the municipal park. The gate was open. Immediately behind it ran a wide, neglected path. The park smelled of cold night and grey sand. This was an old park darkened by tall limes. The limes were already flowering and gave off a faint scent. Only once did the wind blow through the garden and then everything sounded as if it was pouring on them, but the fierce storm abated as quickly as it had come.

At the end of the park there was a steep drop down to the river; beyond it the rainfilled pre-dawn distance, dim lights from the buoys down below, mist, and all the melancholy of a rainy summer's day.

'How do we get down?' asked Kuzmin.

'This way.'

Olga Andreyevna followed the path right up to the edge of the slope and came to some wooden steps stretching away down into the darkness.

'Give me your hand,' Olga Andreyevna said. 'Lots of the steps have rotted through.'

Kuzmin gave her his hand and they carefully began the climb down. The grass growing between the steps was wet from the rain.

At the bottom of the steps they stopped. They could already see the jetty, and the steamer's red and green lights. The steam whistled. Kuzmin's heart contracted as he realized that now he would have to part from this unknown woman who was so close to him, and he could say nothing to her, nothing. He did not even thank her for showing the way, for giving him her small, strong hand in its grey glove, or for carefully guiding him down the decrepit steps: each time she had come across an over-hanging branch that might have brushed his face, she had said 'head down', and Kuzmin had obediently lowered his head.

'I shall leave you here,' said Olga Andreyevna, 'I shan't go any farther with you.'

Kuzmin looked at her. Stern, troubled eyes were looking at him from behind her shawl. Surely this minute, this here and now, would fade into the past and become just another painful memory in her life and in his.

Olga Andreyevna gave her hand to Kuzmin. Kuzmin kissed it and was aware of the same faint smell of perfume that he had first noticed in the dark room with the rain whispering outside.

When he looked up Olga Andreyevna said something, but so quietly that he could not hear. He thought she had said just one phrase, 'in vain'; maybe she had said something else, but from the river came the noise of the steamer chugging angrily and complaining of the dark dawn and its wandering life in the rain and fog.

Kuzmin ran to the bank without looking back, crossed the jetty, went aboard the steamer, and climbed straight on to the empty deck. The steamer was already moving, its paddles working slowly. Kuzmin went astern and looked back at the slope and the steps. Olga Andreyevna was still there. It was almost light now and difficult to see her. Kuzmin raised his hand, but received no answering wave.

The steamer moved farther and farther away, sending back long waves to the sandy banks, rocking the buoys; and the willows on the shore answered the banging of the steamer's wheels with a rushing sound.

Sweet Clover

WEARING his dusty boots, my brother
Tossed in my window a bouquet
From fallow fields: yellow sweet clover . . .
The flower of the drouth, they say.

I left my books, went to the steppeland . . .
The whole field was a golden thing!
And everywhere dots of bees floated
In that dry heat of evening.

And like a net the swarms of insects
Hovered above the saffron field . . .
So: hot and dry again the morrow.
The grain was ripening its yield . . .

. . . And threatening want, destitution,
Perhaps famine. . . . And yet to me
That gold sweet clover for one moment
Was more dear than all else could be.

IVAN ALEKSEYEVICH BUNIN

How They Wrote Robinson Crusoe

IN THE editorial office of the illustrated periodical *Adventure*, there was a shortage of material to grip the imagination of the younger reader.

They had material of a sort, but it was simply not what they wanted. It contained far too much earnest drivel of the kind which, to be quite frank, was more likely to plunge the soul of the younger reader into a murky gloom than to grip his imagination. And the editor insisted on something gripping.

Eventually, they decided to commission a serial story.

The office messenger boy sped off with a summons to the writer Moldavantsev, and, on the very next day, Moldavantsev appeared in the editor's private office and seated himself on the sofa.

'You must appreciate,' the editor tried to ram home the point, 'that it must be something gripping, original, and packed with interest and adventure, in short, a Soviet Robinson Crusoe. The reader must be unable to tear himself away.'

'Robinson Crusoe. Well, I should be able to manage that,' replied the writer curtly.

'But not just Robinson Crusoe, a Soviet Robinson Crusoe.'

'What do you expect, a Rumanian Robinson Crusoe?'

The writer did not waste words. It was evident from the first encounter that this was a man of action. And, sure enough, the story was produced by the deadline. Moldavantsev had made few departures from the famous original. After all, Robinson Crusoe is Robinson Crusoe.

A Soviet youth is shipwrecked. A wave washes him ashore on a desert island. He finds himself alone, defenceless, face to face with the powers of Nature. He is beset with dangers: wild animals, lianas, the onset of the rainy season. But the Soviet Robinson Crusoe, brimful of energy, overcomes every apparently insuperable obstacle. And three years later a Soviet expedition finds him, bursting with life and health. He has conquered Nature, built himself a hut, surrounded it with a green belt of kitchen gardens, bred rabbits, sewn himself a long, belted, blouse from the tails of apes and taught a parrot to wake him in the mornings with the words, 'Attention, attention! Off with the blanket! Time for early morning exercises!'

'Very good,' said the editor. 'The bit about the rabbits is simply magnificent. Extremely apt. But, you know, I am not altogether clear about the basic theme of the story.'

'Man's struggle with nature,' replied Moldavantsev with his usual brevity.

'Very well, but there's nothing particularly Soviet about that.'

'What about the parrot? He takes the place of the radio. A do-it-yourself transmitter!'

'The parrot's very good. And so is the belt of kitchen gardens. But there's no sense of Soviet community life. Where, for example, is the local trade union committee? And the guiding role of the trade unions?'

Moldavantsev suddenly sprang to life. As soon as he sensed that the story might not be accepted, his taciturnity vanished in a trice. He became eloquent.

'What local trade union committee? The island is uninhabited, isn't it?'

'Absolutely correct. It is uninhabited. But there ought to be a local trade union committee. I have no literary pretensions myself, but in your place I should have insinuated one. As a feature of Soviet life.'

'But the whole thing is based upon the idea that the island is uninhabited. . . .' Here Moldavantsev accidentally caught the editor's eye and faltered. The eyes were so Spring-like, so much of the grey bleakness of the month of March was reflected in them, that he decided to try a compromise.

'You're right, of course,' he said, raising his finger, 'why didn't I see that before? There must be two survivors of the shipwreck: Robinson Crusoe and the president of the local trade union committee.'

'And two full-time trade union workers,' added the editor coldly.

'Help!' squeaked Moldavantsev.

'It's no use saying "help". Two full-time workers, and, and one female activist, in charge of collecting membership dues.'

'What do we want her for? Whose membership dues is she going to collect?'

'Robinson Crusoe's.'

'The president can collect Robinson Crusoe's dues. He won't have anything to do.'

'That's where you're wrong, Comrade Moldavantsev. That's completely inadmissible. The president of the local trade union committee can't be allowed to occupy himself with trifles and run about collecting dues. We must fight against this sort of thing. He must occupy himself with serious work, with guiding and leading.'

'We'd better have her then,' conceded Moldavantsev. 'Perhaps it's not a bad idea, after all. She can marry the president or, for that matter, Robinson Crusoe. At any rate, it should make more entertaining reading.'

'There's no need for that at all. Don't go wrapping it up in cheap romance and unhealthy eroticism. Just let her collect her membership dues and keep them in her safe.'

Moldavantsev began to fidget on the sofa.

'Please, there can't be a safe on an uninhabited island!'

The editor became thoughtful.

'Wait, wait,' he said 'there's a splendid passage in your first chapter. Together with Robinson Crusoe and the members of the local trade union committee, the waves deposit various articles on the beach.'

'An axe, a carbine, a compass, a cask of rum, and a bottle of anti-scurvy mixture,' enumerated the writer triumphantly.

'Cross out the rum,' said the editor quickly, – 'and what's all this about anti-scurvy mixture? Who on earth will want that? A bottle of ink would be much better. And a safe is absolutely essential.'

'You've got that safe on the brain! The membership dues can be kept very nicely in the hollow of a baobab tree. Who's going to steal them from there?'

'What d'you mean, who? What about Robinson Crusoe, or the president of the local trade union committee, or the full-time workers, or the store commission?'

'The store commission got washed up as well?' asked Moldavantsev faint-heartedly.

'Certainly.'

A silence ensued.

'Perhaps a table for meetings got washed up as well?' – asked the author venomously.

'O-bligatorily! You must create the conditions for the people to work. Right, you'll need a water-jug, a bell and a table-cloth. The waves can wash up whatever kind of table-cloth you like. A red one, or a green one. I don't wish to inhibit artistic creativity. But the first thing, my lad, is to depict the masses. The broad strata of the workers.'

'The waves cannot wash the masses ashore,' retorted Moldavantsev stubbornly. 'That cuts across the whole idea. Just think! The waves suddenly wash several hundred thousand men on to the beach. It's enough to make a cat laugh.'

'I may say,' interposed the editor, 'a small quantity of healthy, cheerful, spirited laughter never does any harm.'

'No! The waves just couldn't do that.'

'Why the waves?' asked the editor in surprise.

'How else could the masses turn up on the island? It's an uninhabited island, isn't it?'

'Who told you it was uninhabited? You're confusing me. It's all quite clear now. There's this island, or, even better, a peninsula. That would make things easier. And on it there takes place a series of gripping, original, interesting adventures. There's a trade union organization, sometimes not very well organized. The female activist discovers a series of discrepancies, let's say, in the collection of membership dues. The broad masses come to her aid. And the president repents. At the end you can have a General Meeting. That will work out very effectively from an artistic point of view. Well, there you have it.'

'What about Robinson Crusoe?' babbled Moldavantsev.

'Yes. Thank you for reminding me. Robinson Crusoe bothers me. Get rid of him altogether. He's an utterly stupid and quite unjustifiable sniveller.'

'Now I understand,' said Moldavantsev in funereal tones. 'It will be ready tomorrow.'

'Well, that's all. Write away. By the way, there's a shipwreck at the beginning of your story. You know, a shipwreck is quite unnecessary. Let's have it without a shipwreck. It'll be much more interesting. Don't you think so? Very well then. All the best!'

Alone again, the editor smiled happily.

'At last', he said, 'I shall have a real adventure story which is completely artistic as well.'

I'LF and PETROV

Daddy, What Do They Say?

A TALL man in a flapping, brilliantly-coloured shirt stopped for some moments in the glaring sunlight and watched the skies behind the Ukraine Hotel, amass in thick shades of blackish blue.

'It's probably pouring by now up at Fili,' he thought.

And true enough, at Fili all work had been abandoned. People were running over the bulldozed clay for shelter under sheds, trees and news-stands. While trains from the near-by metropolitan line were arriving wet at Belorussky station, dry trains putting out in the opposite direction were being slapped soon afterwards under the downpour, thence to stream on through the rain towards Zhavoronki, Golitsino and Zvenigorod – outskirts where the water streams along hollows, pine-resin fills the air and white churches stand on the hill-tops. He longed to be out there. He felt suddenly like wrapping little Olga up in his coat, picking her up and running with her through the rain to the station. . . .

'Ah, well . . . let's hope it doesn't rain at the stadium,' he said to himself.

Not, as a matter of fact, that he wouldn't have enjoyed playing a game in the rain. In the rain the wet ball hits you as if fired from a cannon, and it's no easy job making a pass: you steel yourself – no nonsense now! You are bound to be accurate, you feel the others all breathing around you, sweating and heavy, the air pressing on you with a sensation of urgency like the alarm bell ringing over a ship at sea; whereas when you're only watching it's best to be up in the stands on a lovely day with a newspaper-hat keeping the sun off your head.

He glanced behind him and called out 'Olga!' In the shade

under a wall a little girl of about six was practising her ballet-steps. She stopped and obediently ran to take her father's hand. They both turned in under the awning of an open-air sandwich-bar calling itself 'Sunny Days'. He looked up again at the mass of clouds, trying to make out which way they were blowing.

'The whole lot might go right past the stadium,' he decided.

The little girl had begun reading a notice. She spelled out the letters aloud, one by one: 'C, U, S, T . . .' In here under the awning it was, if anything, even hotter than out in the street. Customers sat next to the railings, their pink faces aglow with sunlight, sweat glistening in clear beads. It was actually a painful experience to watch them drink hot bowls of soup and eat sizzling-hot mutton-chops.

The little girl was still spelling out letters: 'M, I, S, E . . .'

She stopped. 'Daddy, what do they say?'

He looked at the notice, which strictly forbade customers to drink their own alcoholic beverages on the premises. He was so used to such notices that he had not before paid them any attention.

'What do they say?' repeated the little girl.

'Oh, some nonsense,' he grinned. The little girl looked doubtful.

'Do they really write nonsense in big letters like those?' she asked.

'Oh, yes . . . sometimes.'

He moved over to the far corner in the shade where some friends of his were sitting over some iced beer. His daughter ran up with him. Flaxen-haired, she was wearing a navy-blue sailor-coat and a neat pleated skirt. She had shiny nylon ribbons in her hair and wore white ankle-socks. Every detail about her looked Sunday-best and clean. She resembled the perfect child in the adverts on the side of buses: 'Youngsters know a good jam when they taste one!' Instead of dragging her feet and gazing about, she walked quietly behind her father.

He had once been something of a sportsman. In fact he had
been the champion of his own street and the two neighbouring
ones. Those had been the days when he came home from the
training-fields on spring evenings to be welcomed by all the
local kids streaming out from their gateways to see him. The
girls threw him anxious glances as he passed, and even the most
hardened enthusiasts respectfully touched their caps. A retired
gentleman, a colonel or something, to whom football evidently
meant life itself, stopped him on one occasion and said: 'I hear
you've been coming on. Keep it that way, lad!' He went on in
the special grey cap and navy colours of his team as substitute
for the first eleven. He even walked with that peculiarly gawky
step of professionals, but out of real fatigue – he was not a man
for putting on airs – and he would manage a smile through his
exhaustion.

All that was before Olga had been born and she as yet knew
nothing about it. For him these last six years had passed like
six days. Actually he had already stopped 'coming on' some
time before her birth, although that had not stopped him
playing. Life went on being football all summer and hockey
all winter, and then the same again. Although he got demoted
from the field to the reserves' benches and from them to
the stands, he went on living much as before – football in
summer and hockey in winter . . . six seasons of football, six of
hockey. . . .

Well, is there so much wrong with this? You may drop down
a bit in life – but one should keep to one's own level! Training
between seasons – in autumn and spring we get used to those
flannels! Who wants to be stuck by the telly? Apart from that,
what more can you get out of life? You see, chum, I've got a
wife. Oh, a wife, you say? You mean you keep a wife home in
bed? I mean I have a wife. A wife and little daughter. A daughter
into the bargain with her, eh? Ho, ho! So you didn't forget the
daughter then! Now steady there, mind what you say or you'll

hurt yourself. . . . Ah, well – so it's football and hockey then – and don't you ever get fed up? Look here, what on earth are you saying? How do you think I could get fed up with sport? – In any case there's always my job. And I bet that's some dead-end! Dead end? Stop! No Admittance Except on Business. You don't understand the first thing about my job. All you're interested in is gazing into the sky and making milk turn into yoghurt! Come to think of it they wouldn't let you within a hundred yards of one of our machine-tools. All right, so it's between the football-pitch and the works is it then? Look – how many more times? I've got a wife and child! Ah, but of course you have! I'll give you 'Ah-but-of-course-you-have!' It means there's a family to look after – got it? One-and-a-half-allowance and bonuses? If you want to know, I am a shop-floor rationalizer. Ah, yes – always knew you were the one with the brains up top! Well, let's not, er . . . but anyway I've got plenty of friends there. Look, there they are! Sitting over in the corner there – Petka Strukov and Ildar, Vladik, Zhenechka, Igor Zyamka, the other Petka – yes, they're all here! They've pushed two little tables together. They've splashed out and bought lobster claws by the look of things, and there are puddles on the table already. What a band! All the same age! See – how old are you? Oh, we're all around twenty-nine. And you? . . . Come on, you can count I imagine? mm . . . thirty-two, I make it.

'And what's this here, Sergey, your kid is she?' asked the other Petka. All eyes fixed on the little girl.

'Uh.'

He sat down in the chair which someone pushed out for him and placed the girl on his knee. She was uncomfortable, but sat there quite placidly.

'Sit there and be good, Olga, and in a minute you'll get some sweets.'

They pushed a glass of beer towards him and some lobster on a plate, and he ordered lemonade for the girl and some 'come-an'-have-us' sweets. His friends watched him with huge curiosity. It was the first time they had seen him with his daughter.

'You see Alka's got a conference on all day,' he began explaining to Petka Strukov.

'What, on Sunday?' exclaimed Igor.

'Oh, they have one conference after another – get driven to death.' Sergey smiled ironically, adding, half-guiltily: 'And then her mother went visiting friends so we came along here. . . .'

His eyes crossed to the little girl's head. Her hair was divided down the centre by a thread-like parting.

'Drink that beer,' said Ildar. 'It's cold.'

Sergey lifted up the glass, looked around at his friends, but grinned and had to lower his face to conceal his feelings. To tell the truth he really loved his old football team, and moreover loved each one of them individually. He knew too that they treated him in the same way. It was in fact Sergey whom in some ways they liked best of all, no doubt because it was he who had once been their best player and he had developed before their eyes and played substitute. . . . He was strongly built and had a powerful kick, as well as an eye for the whole field. It had seemed right and natural when he had taken the prettiest of their girls and married her.

Sergey stuck by his friends. It was only in their company that he could retrieve his life of six years ago. Each of them stood firmly by the others, and outsiders were not admitted. They were all as if bound by some secret pact. They carried into their tight circle all their youthful loves and ways, hauling everything together into some unknown future portion of time – which was already past and gone. The way they wore their caps and spoke in haphazard words, their football, hockey, gaudy shirts and evening strolls in the park when Ildar, playing his guitar, sang 'You don't care for me: What do you care?'

But life follows its own laws and forwards and backs got married, transferred to the reserves, were turned into spectators, and made fathers of children. But for all that, children, wives and the whole panoply of everyday life existed somewhere behind the unseen boundaries of their wholly male, Moscow way of life, in which anyone who is late for a match runs to the stadium from the Metro as if staging an attack, and the vast crowd is humming, and everyone is intoxicated by a tremendous feeling of solidarity and spring. None of the friends could understand how it had come about that those girls of theirs (the very same ones who had cheered them on at matches, the very ones they used to dance with!) had become so dependent on them. They played for their department teams, and over glasses of beer recalled their games with the factory team, remembering how one or other of them had been called out as substitute, while Sergey was already playing as substitute, and would have got into the team itself had it not been for marrying Alka. Alas, it was all because of those Alkas, Ninkas, Tamarkas – dependants . . .!

'Daddy, what are you breaking up its head for?' queried the little girl disapprovingly.

Sergey was startled. He caught a glance in those blue eyes, penetrating and severe – Alka's! He let fall the red, beautiful lobster in his hand . . . severe, blue, penetrating look! The look by which Alka had stopped him in his tracks once eight years ago:

'What do you think you are doing? Take your hands off me and come back again when you're sober!'

Could one start laughing with the team now about the wife? Perhaps she really plagues you! Maybe things aren't going so well one way and another – you took it into your head to get to know this swimming or gymnastics teacher in her thirties, and got friendly. . . . But laugh about it under that look?

'Don't pull out its legs.'

'Why not?' he muttered, still absently.

'Because it's a person.'

He put the lobster on the table.

'Well, what do you *want* me to do with it?'

'Hey! Let's have less noise now!' called out Petka Strukov and the neighbouring tables fell silent.

Ildar drew from his pocket a football fixture list and spread it out on the table. Everyone leaned over it and began discussing the team – the team which in their estimation was certain to win the cup but which appeared to be caught up somewhere in the middle region of the table. This was *their* team, which they supported not in the way that uninitiated fanatics cheer on a team they have chosen according to some uncertain principle of selection, but rather in a different way. This was to them the Team with a capital letter, because, simply, it happened to coincide with their highest ideal – the *football team*. Accordingly, in the stands they neither whistled nor stamped their feet; and they would certainly not yell 'Cut out the vodka!' to a player who missed, because they knew that such bad luck can after all happen to anyone, and if you want to know 'Pshenka' could pass anywhere for a first-rate goalkeeper. You see, a ball, right enough, is a round object – but you can't look at a team like that! A team is eleven different lads.

Suddenly out of the street, out of the scorching hot day and into the sandwich-bar, came a man dressed in a light jacket and dark tie. Vyacheslav Sorokin's appearance was noisily greeted:

'Hey there! Good to see you!'

'Hullo! How are things going?'

'What's on in Leningrad?'

'Leningrad's a museum-city,' said Sorokin without elaborating. He began shaking everyone's hand, leaving nobody out.

'Nice to see you, Olga!' he said on getting to Sergey's daughter.

'And nice to see you as well Uncle Vyacha!'

' "Uncle Vyacha"! How did Olga come to know his name I should like to know?' said Sergey to himself. Sorokin took the beer poured out for him and began narrating his Leningrad experiences. He had been sent there as a member of a fact-finding delegation.

'Tremendous monuments of architectural splendour – Rastrelli's works, those of Rossi, Kazakov, the Kvarengians,' lectured Sorokin fluently.

'Well, well, so he picked up a bit of the culture while he was there,' thought Sergey. He too had stayed in Leningrad, playing with the Team. Like any unfamiliar city, Leningrad had excited him, awakening strange feelings in him. But he had been in strict training throughout his stay and allowed himself little time off. He had had no chance even to make friends there, let alone acquaint himself with Leningrad's culture.

'. . . Doric columns, Conic, Gothic, Californic . . .' Sorokin reeled on.

'Oh, that's enough, we don't want to know,' said Sergey.

Everyone smiled. Sorokin tried to look as though he had not been offended. With his fingernail he flicked a piece of lobster-shell off the table and on to the asphalt. Then he leaned his body over the fixture-list. He took a light from Zhenechka's cigarette, remarking that the team would, in his opinion, lose today's match.

'Win today's match,' corrected Sergey.

Sorokin looked straight into Sergey's eyes and said softly: 'I'm sorry, but they'll lose their game, Sergey, you see there are theoretical considerations – the laws of the game must assert themselves. . . .'

'You are talking the purest nonsense, Socky,' smiled Sergey icily.

'Talking nonsense am I?' sprang up Sorokin. 'Now football is a game I happen to have read something about, I'll have you know!'

'Ha! Ha! Ha! Read about it? Listen everyone! Come on, Socky, tell us all about football then!'

Sorokin stiffened and smoothed down his thinning hair with his hand. Smiling as if pitying Sergey, his expression seemed to say, 'Now, Sergey, you've been calling me "Socky" again but you are all on your own there, I am afraid, and no one else is going to follow suit, so your efforts will all be wasted and they'll call me "Slava" as they've always done; and, my dear Sergey, we know all about how you once played for the Team, but that was long ago and it doesn't count now; and although you did in fact succeed in marrying the prettiest one out of all our girl-friends, yet now. . . .'

Sergey reined in his own thoughts with equal success.

'Easy does it, keep it friendly!' he said to himself.

But how exactly do you keep a thing friendly when the friend in question's face makes you want to slosh your beer in it?

Sergey looked away, raising his eyes up to the canvas roof. It bulged as though a fat man were rolling in it. The whole bar was packed to bursting. A gloomy-looking character banged his mug down on the next table. Pushing back his beret from his forehead he declared to everyone loudly:

'I don't come from here see? The old girl is just . . . that's to say we live together, get that straight, see?' The table crashed under his fist. He returned his beret to its former position over his forehead and fell silent, as if he had said all he wanted to say.

Sergey wiped the sweat off his brow. The air was unbearably hot. His eyes met Sorokin's across the table; he heard Sorokin whispering to him: 'You ought to tell your daughter to play outside on the square, Sergey.'

'None of your business,' returned Sergey. Sorokin leaned back in his chair to reassume the pitying smile. Then he leaned forward to rise on his feet and began pulling on his coat: 'I think I'll be on my way, then!'

'Off to the stadium are you?' asked Petka.

'I've no time for that, I'm afraid. I have too much work to do.'

'What – on a Sunday?'

'Well, what can be done about it? I have these exams coming up soon.'

'Which grade are you in now?' asked Zhenechka.

'Grade three.'

'Oh, grade three. Well . . . see you, then.'

'All the best!' Sorokin waved cheerily.

'Here you are, Olga!' he smiled and gave her some chocolate.

'Hold on a minute,' Zyamka called to him.

'We're coming with you. It's too hot in here.'

In a body they rose up and went out into the scorching hot street. Beneath their shoes the asphalt sank like foam rubber, while above their heads the dark mass of clouds had not moved away and was now blackening the sky behind the tall hotel building as if about to culminate in some catastrophe.

'So you'll be along to the stadium,' Sorokin turned affably to Sergey.

'Well, where did you think I'd be going? Did you think I was going to miss a game like today's?'

'Really I don't know I'm sure,' said Sorokin, sighing.

'Well whenever you don't know, try shutting up.'

Sorokin chased across the road after a bus. The rest, talking quietly and occasionally laughing, moved slowly down the shaded side of the street. Usually they would have been making more noise, Zyamka cracking his jokes and Ildar strumming his guitar, but in the little girl's company they felt conscious about their behaviour.

'Where are we supposed to be going to?' asked Sergey.

'We're making for the stadium,' said Igor.

'There's a women's basketball semi-finals on the small field which we can watch until the game begins.'

'Daddy, may I have a word with you a minute?'

Sergey was stopped in his tracks – was it little Olga who had just spoken to him like a grown woman? The others continued walking.

'I thought we were going to the park,' said the little girl.

'No, I'm afraid we're going to the stadium instead. But there is a park at the stadium too, with trees, kiosks and things. . . .'

'And roundabouts?'

'Well, there aren't any actual roundabouts –'

'I want to go to the park.'

'Now be a good girl, Olga.'

'I don't want to go wherever all those men are going,' she continued shamelessly.

'Be a good girl, Olga,' he repeated dumbly.

'Mummy said I could go on the roundabouts.'

'Well she'd better take you then, hadn't she?' Sergey felt irritated. He saw the others waiting on the corner. Olga's face frowned:

'It's no fault of Mummy's she has to go to conferences.'

'Listen!' cried Sergey. 'You lot go on without us! I'll be at the match later.' He pulled Olga's arm:

'Let's hurry up about it, then.'

'Conference after conference,' he thought as they went. 'Damn those eternal conferences. And why did Aunty have to pick today of all days to go out on? What an enjoyable Sunday! And Alka being made Candidate of Science! That tops the lot. I'll have to watch it from now on. It wasn't as if she cared two hoots for me even before this . . .'

His fast strides forced the little girl to run. Her lobster was still wrapped in her handkerchief, its whiskers protruding from the fist of her right hand like aerials from a little radio. She ran cheerfully, reading aloud the letters she saw:

'C-l-o-t-h-i-n-g . . . Daddy?'

'Clothing,' muttered Sergey.

'Meat.'

'Haberdashery.'

Candidate of Science versus Failed Footballer. Perhaps his name was remembered by a few older fans – a hundred out of a hundred thousand. Playing had been tremendous while it had lasted, of course. But it all blew away into nothing . . . he never matched Nette, never went to Syria, never . . . and was it entirely his fault? Madame Candidate, a woman of education as well as of beauty . . . beautiful – yes! But you don't speak with me these days, except at night, when we do still find ourselves with a common language. . . . Throughout the day she'll be talking with other people, like Sorokin for example, who will tell her all about the Kvarengians, etcetera, about all sorts of different columns, getting everything in before you knew he'd started. . . . Two-and-a-half roubles you spent on that? What was that? Did you say something? Two-and-a-half for that? What? Wait! . . . There is neither sport left, nor love. Love? A swimming instructress in her thirties? Not for me, thanks. . . . Stop it! Do you hear! Stop it!

On two grey horses with blue spots they went on the roundabout in the park, Sergey holding his daughter tight while she laughed, quite overspilling with pleasure, sitting the lobster between the two ears of her horse. 'Lobster loves the ride!' she said, her head bobbing up and down. Sergey managed a smile. Just then he noticed his works' chief technician queueing for the roundabout with a little boy. Recognizing Sergey he touched his cap. Sergey disliked to think that he and that greasy and boring man held something in common.

'Your daughter?' the chief technician shouted.

'A big, round, barrel and a bellyful of cotton,' went the music.

'Your son?' shouted Sergey the next time round.

'The young lad's fair lady please,' the song went on.

The chief technician nodded.

'Should-ers.'

'Yes, he's my boy!' shouted the chief technician.

'Not such bad songs they play on the roundabouts! And the old technician's not so bad either.'

And Olga would remember her dazzling roundabout ride for many years.

'Daddy! Shall we tell Mummy about Lobster's lovely ride?'

'Listen, Olga, where did you meet Uncle Vyacha?'

Sergey's words had surprised himself.

'Mummy and I met him on the way to work. He's ever so nice.'

'Hmm . . . ever so nice is he now?' thought Sergey. 'Sock-so-nice. In other words he's up to something. Oh, he's going to get from me what he's been asking for.' He left Olga on a bench while he went into a telephone box and began ringing up that wonderful institute where the wonderful conference was being held. He hoped the conference would have already finished, in which case he would take Olga home, give her to Alka to look after, and then go to the stadium to spend the rest of the day with the lads. Ildar would sing and play his guitar . . .

A groaning buzz came out of the ear-phone. It was finally put an end to by an elderly voice which said:

'Hullo!'

'Has that grand conference of yours finished yet?' asked Sergey.

'Conference? What conference is this?' burbled along the line. 'Today's Sunday . . .'

'Is that the Institute?' shouted Sergey.

'Yes, this is the Institute . . .'

Sergey got out of the box. The air ran in streams like something melting under the heat. Along the road came a fat man panting in a wide-sleeved silk shirt, and trying, tiredly, to shoo away a cloud of flies buzzing around his head. Evidently the flies liked him, for they stayed stubbornly with him. 'So that's it,' thought Sergey. Suddenly he felt as though he would collapse at the knees as an unexpected feeling of fear came over him as if he had been struck on the spine. He would have run out of the park, but remembered Olga. She was sitting on the bench in the shade, playing with her lobster. 'Even lobsters, even lobsters are monsters who go downstairs backwards shaking their whiskers,' Olga passed judgement on lobsters.

'She's talented,' thought Sergey. 'Gets it from her mother.'

He seized her by the hand and pulled. She cried out and showed him the lobster.

'Daddy, he's so clever, he has nearly come alive!'

Sergey stopped and seized the lobster, breaking it in pieces and throwing it into a bush.

'Lobsters aren't toys,' he said, 'they're food. They go with beer.'

The girl burst into tears, in three streams pouring down her face. She refused to move. He took her in his arms and ran. He raced out of the park. Straight away, a taxi turned up. In hot and airless silence the Moscow river flashed below like a wide strip of silver foil, while in front another river unfurled in asphalt – the Sadovoy ring-road, a road which should be flown along, so as to overtake all miserable moods in the race. In his arms sat Olga, who had stopped crying and was beginning to smile. She was enjoying the speed. Letters were flying at her face from advertisements, road-signs, boards and posters – all the letters she had ever learned and thousands more, red, blue, green, circling down to her from the sun's own eleven planets.

'W O R Y W L R W O O E W . . . Daddy, what does *that* say?'

'Worywlrwooew' Sergey pronounced to himself. 'Why so many 'W's'? Worry, weary, wilful, woman, week, whistle, weasel, weak, witch, wife, wedding, wish, wool . . .'

'Daddy . . . what do they say? Just try and read them this fast!'

'Stop the other side of the bridge,' he said to the driver and left him thirty kopeks as shown on the meter.

He ran into his house, jumped up three steps of the staircase, pushed open a door and burst into their flat. All was empty.

Everything was clean, and hot. Sergey looked around and lit a cigarette. The two-roomed flat – his own – seemed so strange and so alien to him that he quite expected someone whom he had never before set eyes on, with whom he had absolutely no connection whatever, to walk in now from the kitchen. He felt queer and shook his head.

'I'm in a bit of a mess aren't I?' he thought with a sigh and switched on the television. He knew at once by the pitch at which the crowd was humming, that the players were about to start.

'Perhaps she's at Tamarka's or Galina's,' he thought.

Going downstairs he assured himself that she was definitely at Tamarka's or Galina's so there was no need to ring. But he went to the nearest phone box and rang. She was not at Tamarka's, or at Galina's. He got out of the box. The sun burnt his shoulders. Olga practised her ballet-steps in the sun. Next to the restaurant were two layabouts from Number 16, standing quietly and peacefully together. Their hands hung down beside their jackets, their crossed fingers flicking. They seemed to be looking for their number three.

The little girl ran up and took his hand.

'Daddy, where shall we go now?'

'Where do you want to go?' he answered. 'We'll go off somewhere if you like.'

They went slowly down the sunny side of the street. Then he decided to cross over.

'What did you spoil my lobster for?' asked Olga complainingly.

'Would you like an ice-cream?' he asked.

'Well, are you having one?'

'Yes, I am.'

Having come through some back-streets they found themselves out on the Arbat, next to a café. Inside the café it was cool and dark. Around all four walls, above the tables, was a continuous mirror. Sergey could see himself coming into the café, with his face red, and his head showing quite large areas of baldness. Olga could not be seen, as she hadn't grown high enough. 'I should think by the look of you you've had quite enough drink for one day already, Sir,' said the waitress on her way past their table.

'Bring us some ice-creams will you?' he called after her. She came up and realized that the man wasn't drunk at all but just had a red face, and his eyes weren't roving under the influence of vodka, but under the influence of something else. Olga ate her ice-cream and dangled her legs to and fro. Sergey ate his ice-cream without noticing what flavour it was – he simply felt the cold in his mouth.

Next to them sat a young couple. The boy, whose hairstyle resembled a sheepskin hat, was trying to influence the girl's mind and persuade her to do something. 'It's not liquidation – call it re-organization,' he said. The girl stared at him, round-eyed.

'Re-demarcation,' he pronounced pleadingly.

She dropped her eyes, and he drew up close to her, murmuring something to her. Their knees could be seen touching.

'Um-um-um,' he murmured, 'possibilities of progress, mur-mur-mur, but possibilities nevertheless, urm-urm-urm, you see?'

She nodded. They got up and went out, swaying slightly.

'Would you like a tortoise, Olga?' asked Sergey.

Olga started and craned her neck.

'Did you say a *tortoise*?' she asked hesitantly.

'A very small live tortoise. There's a pet shop near here. We'll go there now and get a good tortoise for you.'

'Shall we hurry, then?'

They got up and went to the door. From the cloakroom could be heard a radio commentator's muffled yells and, as if coming from the sea, far-away roars from the stadium. Sergey tried to walk quickly past but found it an impossibility. He asked the attendant for the latest score.

First half was over. The team was down. They came out on the Arbat. There were only a few people to be seen, and very little traffic. On days like this everyone went to the country. Across the road was an unusually tall schoolboy. He was wearing his coat unbuttoned, and was all thin and narrow-shouldered, but good-looking and bright. He looked as if he might turn into an athlete and play as centre of the national combined basketball team. For a long time Sergey followed him with his eyes, enjoying the sight of him pacing out the yards, his good-looking head with the smart hair-do bobbing above the crowd. Olga felt carried away by everything in the pet shop. There were birds everywhere – pigeons, green parrots, siskins, canaries! There were fish-tanks with fish flashing and shining in them, like silver powder. Best of all, there was a glazed grotto, which had tortoises inside. The grotto was porous – made of grey painted plaster. Its floor was glass-covered but couldn't be seen for little tortoises all over it. They were huddled tight together, motionless, like cobble-stones. It was as if they were holding their tongues, submitting patiently to the fate which awaited them. Perhaps they were petrified with fear, having been robbed of all confidence in the ability of their shells to protect them, unaware that people don't eat tortoises here, unaware that tortoise doesn't get washed down with beer, but that each of them would be taken, one by one, by a happy little child, to begin a tolerable enough, even if lonely existence. At last a tortoise poked its head out of its shell, mounted atop its neighbour, and began treading over the tops of the others. Where this one thought he was going to, or why, he probably had no idea. But in fact his persistent crawling was making a big impression upon Olga's mind. Dad really and truly bought the tortoise. It was lifted out of its grotto and placed in a box stuffed with grass and full of air-holes.

'What does it eat?' Dad asked the sales-girl.

'Grass,' replied the girl.

'Then what can we give it in winter?' asked Dad, getting interested.

'Hay,' replied the sales-girl.

'We'll have to help with the hay-making this summer, then!' joked Dad.

'What did you say?' said the sales-girl.

'I said we'll have to help with the hay-making this summer.' Dad repeated his joke. The sales-girl looked annoyed and turned away.

The second-half was just starting as they came out into the street. Loud shouting came from almost every window. It was the commentary. Olga carried the box in her hands, and peeped in the holes. It was all dark inside, but a faint rustling could be heard.

'Will she stay alive for very long?' asked Olga.

'Tortoises live to three hundred, so they say,' replied Dad.

'How long will ours live, Daddy?'

Sergey peered inside the box.

'Ours is a young one – about eighteen. Still a boy.'

A roar from the windows signified that the Team had equalized.

'And how long do we live?' asked the little girl.

'Who – us two?'

'You know . . . people.'

'Oh, people don't live very long,' grinned Sergey 'only seventy or a hundred.'

Sounds like quite a fight in there! The announcer will blow up if he keeps shouting like that much longer!

'And then what happens?' asked Olga.

Sergey stopped and looked at her. Alka's penetrating gaze shone from her deep blue eyes.

He bought a packet of cigarettes at a kiosk.

'Then we have soup with the cat.'

Olga smiled. 'Soup with a cat? Daddy, where shall we go next?'

'Let's go on the Lenin Hills,' he suggested.

'Yes, let's!'

The sun sank behind the university, its rays piercing through the building in some places. Sergey lifted up his daughter and sat her upon the parapet.

'Ooooh! Isn't it lovely!' she exclaimed.

A pleasure-launch chugged below. The Lenin Hills sliced the river in two with their shadow, leaving half of it shining in the sun. On the far bank lay the great bowl of the sports arena. You could not see the grass pitch in the middle – only the upper seats of the east block, packed with the crowd. The sound of an announcer's voice wafted up, but the words in it had been lost on the way. Beyond the stadium was a park. There were paths through it, then Moscow . . . Moscow upon Moscow, immense, all ablaze in a sun reflected in a million window-panes! Over there, amongst all that Moscow, were his own thirty-five square metres of home! And out there too, standing at every street corner, was a telephone box of disasters, hearts beating, knees bending and grateful sighs. And strolling the streets quietly were thirty-two-year-olds, whistling and halloing and not finding one another . . . All Moscow full of pretty girls . . . hundreds upon thousands of girls . . . Institutes of higher education conduct research work and promote people . . . Over there is the peaceful place, at his workbench – that's his factory. There he is, now serene, now troubled, now in love – in spring – and now no longer. There he is young – that's his past, incredibly tall as a schoolboy, going through gymnasiums and stadiums, school-halls and beer-halls, dance-halls and front gates, with kissing

and music in gardens. There, too, is everything still to come ...
The future? Soup with the cat.

Sergey held the little girl's hand and felt her pulse beating.
He saw her face out of the corner of his eye, her turned-up nose,
her open mouth with bead-like shining teeth. Suddenly he felt
excited, as if the answers to all his problems were coming to him,
as if he saw his daughter growing up, and being eight years old,
and becoming fourteen ... sixteen ... eighteen ... twenty! She
would go to holiday-camp with her school-friends, and come
back afterwards, and he himself would teach her to swim, and
she'd start dressing like a woman and looking smashing, and be
kissing some bloke in a doorway, and he'd yell at her ...
They'd sometimes go out together, he'd take her somewhere, to
the sea-side perhaps.

Olga drew her finger through the air, writing invisible letters.

'Daddy, guess what I'm writing.' He watched the little finger
whirling around above the stadium and encircling Moscow.

'I don't know,' he said. 'Can't guess at all.'

'Oh, Daddy, but you're not trying! Now watch!'

And she began writing out on his hand:

'O-l-g-a, D-a-d-d-y.'

A powerful roar, as big as an explosion, came from the stadium,
telling Sergey the Team had scored again.

Prayer

GIVE me fever, insomnia, short-windedness,
Years of malady – bitter and long.
Take away my own child and my sweetheart
And the cryptic, divine gift of song.
During Thy Liturgy this I pray, Lord,
After so many harrowing days,
So that clouds which are darkening Russia
Will grow white in a burst of sun-rays.

ANNA AKHMATOVA

The Dynamo Team: Legend and Fact

THIS almost incredible story occurred in the summer of 1942, and it was so popular that at one time people referred to the ravine as, 'the self-same Babi Yar where they shot the soccer players.' In those days it made the rounds in the form of a legend, one so fine and so satisfying that I want to set it down in full. Here it is:

Kiev's Dynamo soccer team had been one of the best in the country before the war. Its fans knew all about the players, especially the famous goalie Trusevich.

Because of the encirclement, the team had been unable to get away from Kiev. At first they sat tight, found work wherever they could and kept in touch. Then, longing for soccer, they began to hold practice in a vacant lot. The boys in the neighbourhood discovered this right away, then the adults, and finally the German authorities.

They called in the players and said, 'Why use a vacant lot? Look, here is an excellent stadium going begging, so by all means practise there. We have nothing against sports, in fact, the opposite.'

The Dynamo men agreed and moved into the stadium. Sometime later the Germans summoned them again and said, 'Kiev is returning to normal; the movie theatres and the opera are open, and it's about time we opened the stadium too. Let everyone see that peaceful restoration is in full swing. We offer you a match against the all-stars of the armed forces of Germany.'

The Dynamo men asked for time to think it over. Some were against it on the grounds that playing soccer with the fascists would be disgraceful treason. Others felt differently: 'On the contrary, we'll whip them, humiliate them in front of all the people and raise the morale of the Kievans.' This side won. The team began to train in earnest under its new name, 'Start'.

Bright posters appeared on the streets of Kiev:

SOCCER
GERMANY'S ARMED FORCES ALL-STARS
vs.
CITY OF KIEV ALL-STARS

The stadium was filled; half of the stands were occupied by the Germans and all their important leaders, including the commandant himself. They were in fine spirits and expected a happy outcome. The poorer seats were occupied by the hungry, ragged populace of Kiev.

The game began. The Dynamo men were emaciated and weak. The well-fed German team played a rough game, openly tripping their opponents; but the referee noticed nothing. The Germans in the stands roared with glee when the first goal was scored against the Kiev team. The other half of the stadium kept gloomily silent: now they were spitting on us in soccer.

Then suddenly the Dynamo men seemed to rally. They were seized with fury. They drew strength from unknown sources. They outplayed the Germans and, with a desperate surge, drove home the equaliser. Now the German rooting section subsided into a disappointed silence, and the rest of the crowd screamed and embraced.

The Dynamo team recovered its pre-war finesse and, with some brilliant teamwork, scored its second goal. The ragged crowds shouted, 'Hurrah!' and 'They're licking the Germans!'

This 'licking the Germans' remark overstepped the bounds of sportsmanship. Germans swept through the stands shouting, 'Stop that!' and firing in the air. The first half ended and the teams left the field for a rest.

An officer from the commandant's box visited the Dynamo locker room during the intermission and very politely told them,

'Well done, you've played good soccer and we appreciate it. You have upheld your athletic honour sufficiently. But now in the second half, take it easy; because as you yourselves must realize, you have to lose. You must. The German army team has never lost before, especially not on occupied territory. This is an order. If you don't lose, you'll be shot.'

The Dynamo men listened in silence and then went out to the field. The referee blew his whistle and the second half began. The Kiev team played well and scored a third goal. Half of the stadium was roaring, and many wept for joy; the German half was grumbling with indignation. Dynamo kicked in another goal. The Germans in the stands leaped to their feet and fingered their pistols. Guards ran out along the sidelines and cordoned off the field.

It was a game to the death, but the people in our section did not know it and so they kept up their joyful shouting. The German players were utterly crushed and dispirited. The Dynamos scored again. The commandant and all the officers left the stands.

The referee cut the game short with his whistle. The guards, not even waiting for the teams to reach the lockers, grabbed the Dynamo players right there on the field, loaded them into a closed truck and took them off to Babi Yar.

Nothing of this kind had ever happened in the history of soccer. In this game, however, athletics was purely political from start to finish. Because the Dynamo players had no other weapons, they turned soccer itself into a weapon and accomplished a truly deathless exploit. They had known victory meant death, but they had won anyway, in order to remind the people of their dignity.

In actuality, the story was not quite so tidy. The ending was the same, but like all things in life, the events were more complicated. Not one game, but several, took place, and the fury of the Germans mounted from match to match.

The Dynamo players wound up in occupied territory not because they had been unable to get away but because they had been in the Red Army and were captured. Because a large part of the team went to work as loaders at Bakery No. 1, in time they were enlisted in the bakery team.

There was a German stadium in Kiev, but Kievans were not admitted. But posters really did go up on July 12, 1942:

OPENING OF UKRAINIAN STADIUM
The Ukrainian Stadium will open at 4 P.M. today
(Bolshaya Vasilkovskaya, 51, entrance
on Prozorovskaya).
Opening programme: gymnastics, boxing, track and
field events and, most interesting, a soccer match
(at 5.30 P.M.)

The team of some German army unit really was defeated in that game, and the Germans didn't like it; but no arrests occurred. The Germans, annoyed, simply signed up the stronger PSG army team to play the next game, on July 17. Start routed, literally routed, this team, 6–0.

The newspaper report of that game was priceless:

... But this victory can hardly be called an achievement on the part of the Start men. The German team was made up of fairly strong individual players, but was not a team in the full sense. This is not surprising, for the team consisted of players who were in the unit for which they were playing by chance. Another factor was the Germans' lack of practice, without which even the strongest team could accomplish nothing. The Start team, as everyone well knows, consists mainly of former players for the select Dynamo team, so one would expect them to make a far better showing than they actually made in this match.

The ill-concealed irritation and the note of apology that permeated every line of this commentary were only the beginning of the tragedy.

On Sunday, July 19, Start played against a Hungarian team, MSG Wal, and won 5–1. This is from the report on that match:

> Despite the final score, the two teams can be considered almost equally strong.

The Hungarians proposed a return match, which was held on July 26. The final score: 3–2, in favour of Start. Now it looked as though the team was ready to be beaten, and the Germans would have their gratification.

A new match was announced for August 6 between Start and the 'most powerful', 'mightiest', 'undefeated' German Flakelf team. The newspaper went simply wild in its advance coverage of the Flakelf team, citing its fabulous record of goals scored and prevented and other such statistics. This was the match described in the legend that culminated in that German defeat. The newspaper carried no report of it. However, the soccer players were not arrested yet. On August 9, a small notice appeared in *Novoye Ukrainskoye slovo*:

> A friendly match between the best football teams of the city, Flakelef and Start (from Bakery No. 1), will be held at Zenith Stadium at five o'clock this evening.

Start was getting another chance. But it defeated the Germans in this game, too; and on August 16 it beat the Ukrainian nationalist Rukh team by a score of 8–0. After this game the Dynamo soccer players were finally sent to Babi Yar.

This was at the time when there was heavy fighting on the Don and the Germans had reached the approaches to Stalingrad.

Conscience

One can have peace of mind by agreeing,
For convenience, to call evil good.
But then what should one do,
                                        one whose conscience
Unexpectedly unmasks its hood?
What to do here when shame comes arriving
In a man, telling him why it came?
Accidentally, eventually, may it happen –
Like the trumpets of angels –
                                        that shame!
Human shame,
                    the great god,
                                        cruel, ancient,
Used to run through the groves with the blade
Of its dagger hid, dressed like mad Furies,
For its victim who trembled, afraid.
And though years flew by, it still pursued him,
Caught him when he expected it least:
Midst a battle,
                        in bed with his woman,
Or while raising a glass at a feast.
I don't know of a miracle greater!
Even now it's an unexplained plan.
I don't know from what place came our conscience,
Where it originated in man.
Choked or not, it will live on forever;
It's Earth's lasting reward for all plights.

One should marvel not at the soul's baseness
But, instead, at its measureless heights.

From Post-War Years

A YEAR ago a comrade working on archives sent me a copy of a tsarist Security Police document: 'Extract from an unsigned letter obtained through an agent, sent from Moscow on 17th November 1908 to Sergey Nikolayevich Shestakov in Kiev: "... From Poltava I travelled by way of Smolensk to Moscow. Outwardly things are pretty bad here: I have to put up for the night in odd places; in spite of many acquaintances it is hard to find a night's lodging. The impression I gathered in general about Moscow and from our friends in particular is that, however depressing things are, they are relatively satisfactory compared with the south. I would not say that the situation is any better than it was in the spring, but at least it is no worse. Many people are convinced that the Party crisis is coming to an end. At the recent regional conference a certain re-animation of the work was noted, especially in Ivanovo-Voznesensk, Sormovo and in the Moscow district. As you know from the Press, the Moscow district committee was arrested the other day. With regard to tactical points I must tell you first of all about the Moscow committee's resolution which was passed with certain amendments by the regional conference. Its main propositions are: a general international sharpening of class contradictions, the end of a certain revival in Russian capitalism, the mongrel social-reformist trend among the *bourgeoisie*, the abomination of the government's agrarian 'reform', the impossibility of a successful economic struggle – and the way out to be political ferment, the inevitability of a revolutionary upsurge with a more proletarian and international character. In the way of practical tasks the Party notes the necessity to establish closer relations with the proletariat in the West, to form a strong underground organization, the desirability of a stricter Socialist approach to the work and also the need for sterner methods of influencing the parliamentary group. This last has begun to behave better: it has passed a resolution accepting the leadership of the Central Committee, and the deputy Beloussov even made a speech on the agrarian question the text of which was written by Lenin. It has also come out officially with a statement on its disagreement with the deviating Bolsheviks. These have gained the support of Plekhanov, Martov and Dan, who have declared that illegal work now is not only inexpedient but positively harmful. The editorial board of the *Golos Sotsial-Demokrata* (The Voice of the Social-Democrat), that is, the Caucasian Mensheviks headed by Kostrov, do not accept this. Number 8–9 of the *Golos S.D.* is not to be found in Moscow, but No. 30 of *Proletarity* (The Proletarian) has been received" '.

As I read this letter I did not immediately recognize its author and thought he must have been some old Bolshevik, a comrade of mine in bygone days. But when I got to the address it suddenly came back to me. At the end of the letter a note had been added: 'In the opinion of the Police Department the writer of this letter is Ilya Ehrenburg who is under police surveillance'. The Police Department was not mistaken; it is indeed a copy of a letter I wrote to Valya Neumark. Re-reading it I was less surprised by its contents than by its language, in rather the same way as one finds it difficult to recognize oneself on an old photograph.

When I wrote those words about the misdeeds of the Duma faction I was not yet eighteen. A year later I wrote the following verses: 'I have taken leave of your loud bold songs, of the banners rebelliously raised to heaven, because the camp was too narrow for me.'

Some of my readers have been baffled by the sudden and swift transformation of an adolescent, fanatically engrossed in illegal political work, into a youth writing decadent verse. On arriving in Paris I was tremendously attracted to art and discovered a whole new world. However, I continued to attend meetings and the reading of political reports and hoped to make my way back to Russia to resume underground work. I made it clear that in these memoirs I should leave out certain things, but, as I have said, my short stay in Vienna played an important part in my giving up political work. While there I lived at X's (I omit the name). It is possible that the impressions of a raw youth may seem to be presented with hindsight. My job was a simple one: I pasted the Party paper into a cardboard cylinder round which I packed art reproductions and then posted it to Russia. X was kind to me and when he learnt that I wrote verse he talked to me several evenings about poetry and art. He did not so much express opinions open to debate as categorical assertions. Later, at the first Congress of Writers, I heard similar assertions. In 1934 I was forty-three and had had time to look round and to understand a few things. But in 1909 I was eighteen and quite unable to see ahead or comprehend the march of history. To X the poets I admired most were 'decadents', 'a product of political reaction'. He talked about art as something of secondary importance, a by-product, and I went back to Paris bewildered and depressed: I felt as if I had been robbed of everything. I told Liza that I did not know how to live through the next day.

A reader has sent me a few early poems of mine printed in various magazines. These poems (incredibly feeble) have enabled me to recapture the torments of those far-off years; I felt I had lost my way: 'Sad and humble, humble in the dust, autumn roads, whither have you led me?' I scoffed at my own verses: 'Enough! I know both haughty posturing and cardboard breastplates. Down to earth, down to earth! Fight the enemies! I am once again a warrior begrimed with dust. Take me under your red banner! I am worthy of the armour of old.'

The letter written so long ago gave me pause. Valya Neumark, the Social-Democratic deputies to the Duma, and X who shattered me with his dogmatic pronouncements on the utilitarian essence of art, have been dead these many years. My life lies behind me and I can only say that there is a thread connecting the letter of the adolescent with the old writer's memoirs. I do not regret having started to work in the underground Bolshevik organization at the age of fifteen, nor that three years later, having in the meantime become infatuated with poetry, I stopped going to meetings; for a few months longer I attended the *Haute Ecole des Etudes sociales* but finally I dropped this too, read the old and the new poets from morning till night, gazed at pictures and listened to discussions about Cubism and 'scientific poetry'.

Nevertheless, even in those years I could not forget what at fifteen had seemed to me the simple and unique truth; I listened with emotion to people coming from Russia, I made a pilgrimage in May to the *Mur des Fédérés*, I hated the flash and falsehood of the world of money. Anyone who has read these memoirs thus far will know that all my life I tried, for my own satisfaction, to link justice with beauty and the new social order with art. The two Ehrenburgs in me seldom lived at peace with one another; often the one would subjugate and even trample on the other; there was no duplicity here but the uneasy fate of a man who made a great many mistakes and yet passionately abhorred the idea of treachery.

Critics seldom try to understand a writer, they have other things to do; occasionally (for the most part on special anniversaries) they extol but more often they decry him. Western journalists have accused and still accuse me of tendentiousness, of political bias, of subjecting truth to narrow ideology and even to directives from higher up. Some Soviet journalists on the other hand have contended, and still contend, that I suffer from excessive subjectivity, but equally from objectivity, that I am unable to separate the new awareness of reality from the rubbish of obsolete emotions, that I portray unrepresentative characters and am an advocate of formalism. I have no intention of defending my books about several of which I have myself expressed fairly harsh opinions in these memoirs; my present subject is not literary shortcomings but my past. *Men, Years – Life* is not a novel and I could neither change the plot nor alter the main character's traits. If I have said nothing about certain events in my life, I have at least been frank about my errors and irresponsibility. In extenuation I may say that inner inconsistencies and contradictions of this kind have equally affected many of my contemporaries; they would appear to be inseparable from our particular epoch.

My character was formed by the traditions, the ideas and the moral values of the nineteenth century. Today it all seems like ancient history, but in 1909, when I filled exercise-books with wretched verse, Tolstoy, Korolenko, Anatole France, Strindberg, Mark Twain, Jack London, Bloy, Brandes, Synge, Jaurès, Kropotkin, Bebel, Lafargue, Pèguy, Verhaeren, Rodin, Degas, Mechnikov and Koch were still alive. I do not repudiate either the boy with his prickly hair-cut, who condemned the 'deviators' and scoffed at Nadya Lvova's enthusiasm for poetry, nor the raw youth who, after discovering Blok, Tyutchev and Baudelaire, was outraged by talk of the minor and essentially subsidiary role of art; today I understand them both.

My eagerness for revolutionary struggle and my work in the illegal Bolshevik organization were not wasted, they predetermined much of my life and, if they prevented me from getting a secondary education – for instead of going to school I spent my days at secret assignations, at meetings, in workers' hostels and cafés, and later in a prison cell – they taught me a great deal. Of course what pitched me into starting life in this particular way were the events of 1905, my older comrades, especially my friend Nikolay, a pupil at the gymnasium, and books, but more than anything it was my own character that prompted this decision.

In 1917 I did not at first recognize that this was what I had been fighting for ten years earlier: in exile I had lost touch with Russian life and had developed an enthusiasm for other values, real or illusory, which, it seemed to me, were being trodden underfoot. Two years later I realized my mistake. Certain friends wanted me to join them in Paris but I went to Moscow instead. Of my own free will I attached myself to the idea which at first I saw as Gogol's winged troika and later as a State chariot, a tank, a sputnik. In 1957 I wrote: 'In deep autumn, from the dense Russian forest, in the cold and sadness of the countryside, it was sent up into the skies by the hope and despair of man . . . I do not know whether they will realize, whether they will understand . . . For forty years it has been storming above me, the sputnik of my hopes and of my anxiety, incredible, remote and yet my own.'

I put many of my doubts into the mouth, or rather into the diary, of one of the characters in *The Second Day*. Volodya Safanov hangs himself, and that was I trying to hang myself. I made myself keep silent about many things in the years of the swastika, of the Spanish war, of the life-and-death struggle. The epoch which is now referred to as 'the personality cult' added a forced silence to the voluntary one.

I might have been arrested, as so many of my friends were, during the years of arbitrary rule. I do not know what Babel's thoughts were when he died; he was one of those whose silence was not just a matter of caution but one of loyalty. I might have died in the post-war years, before the 20th Congress, like Tairov, Suritz and Tuwim. They, too, suffered anguish over the crimes committed, allegedly in defence of ideas which they shared and for which they felt themselves responsible. I am lucky to have lived to see the day when I was summoned to the Writers' Club and given Khrushchev's report on the cult of the individual to read.

It is far easier to change policy and the economic system than to alter human consciousness. I often come across people who have been unable to divest themselves of a sense of constriction, of fear, of casuistry, of survivals from the past. But a generation is now growing up which has not known 'stormy applause becoming an ovation', or nights of listening for a step on the staircase. The period of transition from religious beliefs to a scientific awareness of reality was very protracted; but the young people born in the early forties advanced in a single day from blind faith to critical thinking. One can only express gratitude yet again to those who were courageous enough to see that the exposure of arbitrariness meant strengthening the ideas of the October Revolution. And my greatest joy is to listen to the opinions, sometimes immature but always sincere and outspoken, of our young people on the threshold of life.

With the years I have come to realize that both my love for art and my loyalty to the idea of Socialism are an inseparable part of one overriding interest: the fate of culture. When I began life culture was the creation and possession of the few. Now in our country, in some form or other and to a greater or less degree, culture has reached almost everyone. For close on fifty years people have been reading and thinking, and they have grown spiritually. During the years that *Novy Mir* has been publishing these memoirs I have received a great many letters; my contemporaries recall the past and speak of their anxieties and hopes, while the young people ask questions about those eternal problems of the meaning of life which in the old days used to be quite unjustly termed 'accursed'; all these letters have taught and inspired me.

I have frequently referred to my mistakes. Mistakes have been made by others, too, and by society as a whole – the list is long – a fact not forgotten by our opponents nor yet by our own people.

During the post-war years I have often visited the West. The standard of life has risen compared with pre-war days, the new industrial style in architecture and household goods has become paramount, life has grown more comfortable and also more restless. Peace of mind has disappeared not only as a result of the increase in mechanization but also because of the uncertainty of the morrow. I have witnessed the collapse of the Fourth Republic and the dismantling of the British Empire. It is only in the USA that one still hears apologias of capitalism, while the statesmen of Western Europe, with their talk of planned economy, sectors of nationalization and higher income-tax, try to make others believe that just by standing still they are keeping in step with the times.

I think that many of our mistakes, material and spiritual, arise from the fact that early morning is not high noon and that, as the French say: *si jeunesse savait, si vieillesse pouvait.* It is easy enough to dash along the well-known roads of the past in a smooth-running, completely up-to-date car. But to find your road into the future is another matter; you often go astray and there is no one to ask the right way to your destination.

The world has altered greatly. When I entered conscious life despots and reactionaries were said to lack logic; Cartesianism was still alive. Half a century of history and the experience of each one of us have proved that the old logic is indeed bankrupt; impeccable hypotheses have been confuted by events; life has developed not in accordance with Descartes's laws but often in violation of them. There is no difficulty in explaining the past with the help of dialectics. But what worries me is how does a man conduct his personal life when he is confronted with situations unforeseen both by his favourite authors and at the many conferences and discussions he has attended?

When I was a boy, Russian, German and Italian schoolchildren were taught that it was sinful to kill, to steal, to fail to honour one's parents, to envy other people's happiness; they knew the Ten Commandments by heart. In French schools, after the disestablishment of the Church, a new subject, ethics, was introduced: the Ten Commandments were given a new look with the help of La Fontaine's fables, and the articles of the criminal code were embellished by quotations from Victor Hugo. The building of a house does not begin with the roof, and later generations will refer to the confused twentieth century as an epoch of great scientific, social and technical discoveries, but not as a time of the harmonious development of man. In our days the acquiring of knowledge is in advance of moral education the world over, physics is leaving art behind and people are approaching an era of nuclear-propulsion unequipped with the brakes of genuine morals. Conscience is not a religious idea, and Chekhov, who was by no means a believer, had a most sensitive conscience (as had other representatives of Russian nineteenth-century literature). I believe that it is imperative to rehabilitate the idea of conscience. But that is perhaps to overstep the proper bounds of this chapter and of the entire book.

I remember one of our lecturers saying in 1932 that Einstein's discoveries meant the revival of idealism and even mysticism. The new science encountered many unexpected obstacles: birth pangs are never easy. In a matter of thirty years the scientists' achievements became so clear that the average man's awareness of reality was radically altered. Nineteenth-century science looks to us now like a snug little dwelling. Something of the same sort, though on a smaller scale, must have happened to people at the time of the late Renaissance when they realized that the Earth was not the centre of the universe. The idea of infinity presents itself to us in a new light now. What formerly seemed absolutely real has become an abstraction, and yesterday's abstraction is becoming a reality.

When the development of physics and its role in the making of nuclear weapons was finally grasped by politicans, military men and also by ordinary people, everyone realized the possibility of life on our planet being annihilated. There are two solutions open to us: either to stockpile nuclear weapons or to agree to general disarmament. I continue to travel about attending peace councils and conferences and 'Round Table' meetings. Sceptics sometimes remind me of the past – of The Hague Convention and of the Amsterdam Congress held before the Second World War – and tell me I am naïve. But I think it is the sceptics who are naïve. Formerly disarmament was the idealists' Utopia – or else the hypocrisy of robbers. When one tiger suggested to another that fangs should be drawn and claws clipped they hoped in this way to reassure the many millions of flocks of sheep. Today the tigers realize that nuclear war is not a question of strategic plans, not a question of who has most oil, steel or even uranium, but one of instant and general annihilation. Disarmament has become a vital necessity for us all, and if arguments about the way it is to be achieved still go on, it is only because tradition is far stronger in international politics than in science. There is only one question, namely, whether the warnings of the physicists will outstrip the routine of the diplomats so that governments realize the necessity of passing from talk to action before some stupid accident leads to catastrophe.

Life is full of contradictions. There are people who talk of co-operation in the conquest of outer space, about flights to the moon, and who at the same time (fortunately, in words only) are prepared to blow up this poor planet because they cannot reach agreement with others about the status of the sectors of one city. The age-old habit of settling disputes by force of arms today impels various States to equip themselves with atomic weapons. In my youth it used to be said that one cannot live beside a powder-barrel; today we live close to far more dangerous barrels. Scientific knowledge has outstripped wisdom.

In the second half of the twentieth century art has had to yield to other things everywhere. To all appearances it has gained ground: the output of novels has increased in almost every country, the number of people who go to picture galleries and exhibitions has grown, the cinema and television have become part of everyday life. Nevertheless, the role of art and letters in the personal life of very many people has diminished. This may have come about because the voice of art has been drowned by the more resounding changes in science and in social life. Or it may be that these changes have led to a certain decline of interest in art: people have lost their peace of mind; they marvel at sputniks, fear nuclear bombs, are enchanted by new inventions, behave like lunatics at sports events and eagerly look forward to machines that will transform semi-fabricated foodstuffs into Lucullan feasts.

Certain notable inventions, like television, provide a daily substitute for art. People go less often to the theatre and instead of reading a book settle down in front of the television set. Fighting in the Congo and the Olympic games, the weddings of queens and the funeral of a president, ballerinas and perform- ing cats, Hamlet and boxers, concerts and scandals in high society flit across the screen. All this flickers, clatters, thunders and mews; poetry mingles with advertisements, music with weather forecasts. People watch, and at the same time eat, gossip and quarrel, while the faculty for receiving impressions is blunted.

I remember that in my childhood people spoke of Tolstoy with reverence. They regarded him as a prophet. When Zola was condemned for defending Dreyfus the entire world was stirred. During the years of the First World War those who had not lost their heads listened to the voice of Romain Rolland. Paris audiences came to blows over Stravinsky's music and Picasso's décor. Today fighting may break out occasionally, but between fans at a football match.

It was entirely my own fault that some five years ago a dis- cussion was launched in *Komsomolskaya Pravda* on whether art was doomed in the 'atomic age'. One of the cybernetics experts jeered at the young people who felt passionately about art and, as he put it, were always gushing 'Ah, Blok! Ah, Bach!' I read thousands of letters on the subject, some addressed to me personally and others to the paper. Almost all the young people – girls and men – were horrified at the thought that art might be dying out; but the cybernetics expert found a hundred sympathizers who vaunted the grandeur of science as opposed to music and poetry; their arguments were a mixture of technocratic ideals and the utilitarianism of Turgenev's Bazarov.

If these people's prognostications were to be proved right then it would follow that the conquest of outer space would be undertaken by inferior beings with the necessary knowledge but devoid of either culture or sensibility, and in fact differing little from the thinking-machines of the twenty-first century. The discovery of fire, that is, of how to make it, goes back to the Stone Age. Tens of thousands of years later Aeschylus wrote *Prometheus Bound*. This tragedy lives on, and still today inspires millions of people, quickening man's feeling of personal dignity. Even flies have sexual impulses, but for love to be experienced thousands of years of art were needed – from the Minoans and Kālidāsa to Goethe, Stendhal, Tolstoy and on to Apollinaire, Blok, Mayakovsky, Hemingway, Eluard and Pasternak.

I believe that a new perception of reality, new modes of feeling, demand a new language of art. For people who knew only Giotto's painting and Rutebeuf's poetry, Villon, Rabelais and Paolo Uccello must have represented the decadence of art, while four hundred years later, for the French of the Second Empire, brought up on classicism and romanticism, Manet, Degas, Baudelaire and Flaubert appeared barbarians, trampling on beauty.

At the Leningrad meeting of the European Writers' Community, someone said that it was better to follow on the lines of Tolstoy, Dickens and Stendhal than on those of Proust,

Kafka or Joyce. I do not believe that our times leave the artist no alternative but to choose whose imitator he prefers to be.

It is inevitable that I should have devoted so much space to art in these memoirs: it is a matter that touches closely not only my craft but also my perception of the world. I am convinced that one cannot go forward on one foot alone; I believe that without beauty to satisfy the spirit no social changes, no scientific discoveries will give mankind true happiness. The argument that in art both form and content are dictated by society, however true, seems to me too formal. Of course, Leonardo da Vinci and Michelangelo knew more and felt more acutely and more deeply than their contemporaries, and of course they had to take into account the patrons, the cardinals, the princes, even the paid assassins of their time. But whether eulogized or persecuted, they were the philosophers, the discoverers who paved the way to the future. Their works still move us deeply today, whereas the history of Italian towns at the close of the fifteenth and the beginning of the sixteenth century strikes us as disorderly, bloody and altogether unattractive, though fortunately long over and done with. Was not Stendhal more perceptive, more profound than his contemporaries – the subjects of the 'good king with an umbrella'? During his lifetime *Le Rouge et le Noir* was read by thousands of people of whom perhaps only a couple of hundred discerned its true value. Here was certainly no imitator. He grew out of his century, and outgrew it. His novels repelled many people, they angered even Balzac and Goethe who dimly sensed Stendhal's power. And could anyone claim that Pushkin's poetry, Lermontov's *A Hero of Our Times* and Gogol's *Dead Souls*, those works of genius, are mere reflections of the Russia of Nicolas I: no more than the concentrated products of the ideas and emotions of the progressive nobility of the epoch?

Wiener's book on cybernetics seemed to me enthralling but it did not make me sing a requiem for art. On the contrary, it made me realize how swiftly everything changes in our epoch. Literature and painting will change too. There is nothing worse than to indulge in the grousing of old age, critical of the times and of the younger generations, accusing them of not knowing how to aspire or suffer as their grandfathers did. Of that failing, at least, I am guiltless.

I am ending the story of my life at the onset of that period which must be my last and of which I do not care to write, namely, the present decade. Since the beginning of 1954, when I finished *The Thaw*, ten years have gone by. I have continued travelling all over the world, I have read books by new writers, I have met friends, I have loved, I have suffered and I have hoped.

In some ways I have lived more intensely and at times more vividly than when I was young. It seems that I had not yet plumbed the depths of certain emotions, nor heard the voice of quiet, nor appreciated to the full the glory of the last sunny days of late autumn.

Early in 1963 I spent two days with Picasso. I looked at his new series of pictures *The Rape of the Sabines*. It was David's painting that had given him the idea of the composition. According to the legend the Romans who wanted wives kidnapped the Sabine women, and when the Sabines came to make war on Rome, the women, who by that time had borne children, stopped the bloodshed. What Picasso created, however, was not a touching reconciliation but an apocalyptic vision of war, new *Guernicas*, in which every inch of the canvas is telling. I stood in the studio entranced and only during the night thought to myself: it's really extraordinary; after all, he's over eighty.

I went to many countries I had never seen before: India, Japan, Chile and Argentina; the world expanded for me: in my youth I had known only Europe and, by hearsay, the USA – one and a half continents instead of five. I met many people who seemed to me important, such as Jawaharlal Nehru, with whom

I had a conversation in Delhi and who struck me as being in politics what Amrita Sher-Gil's pictures are in art: a true amalgam of Indian national profundity and progressive western thought.

I went to Armenia and fell in love with the country; its pink-tinged aridity reminded me of Castile. I liked the people, who are passionately attached to their land, though by no means narrow or provincial but genuine citizens of the world. Saryan painted my portrait; he talked of the past and grew very heated about people who cared nothing for art; he might have been a novice painter in the first flush of excitement over ochre and cobalt instead of a very old man. In 1965 Saryan attained the age of eighty-five and his early paintings were put on exhibition: pictures of dogs in Constantinople, of Egyptian palm trees and Persian women. There was a film about him for which I wrote the script. I described how the artist's work had been hampered and how, in 1948, he had taken down his finest paintings from the walls and slashed them to pieces. I felt – remembering my own book *The Ninth Wave* – that I could well understand the painter's feelings.

I went on deriving great joy from art which continuously opened my eyes to fresh things. The invention of cinemato-graphy is a technical achievement, but after seeing Fellini's and Alain Resnais's latest films I realized that the cinema had found a language of its own; that it could present not only the acting of that superlative mime, Charlie Chaplin, visual reality and the dynamics of events, but also shed light on the airless, dark places of man's spiritual world in a different way from that shed by the theatre, the novel and painting.

I enjoyed the precision of Salinger's novel about an adolescent, and many books and stories by our own young writers, like Kazakov and Aksenov, gave me great pleasure. After reading the short and, on the face of it, conventional story by Solz-henitsyn, I felt enriched: not in Chekhov's manner but with

Chekhov's depth the author had introduced into my world a wonderful Russian woman who had grappled with great difficulties.

In the last few years there have been many deaths among old friends: Falk, Nezval, Joliot, Rivera, Konchalovsky, Pasternak, Zabolotsky, Hemingway and Nazim Hikmet. I am very conscious of the thinning of the forest of my life. I look with almost superstitious solicitude at those of my friends still living, and in the evenings I find solace in memories of the friends of my youth.

I have got to know Konstantin Paustovsky: in the old days I hardly ever met him; I always knew him as a talented writer and now I have found in him a noble-hearted, kind and courageous man. We have become friends in our old age. It makes me glad to think that Paustovsky is alive; that tomorrow he will say more; that he is my contemporary who has lived through many of the things I have described in these memoirs; that he is not only a great craftsman but a man of sensitive conscience and that in the spring of 1963, at a difficult time, he came to me and comforted me.

I have also become much attached to Victor Nekrassov, a bold and intelligent writer. I have found that old age is not a blank wall: it, too, has its windows and a door.

I do not seem to have lost the capacity to love or hope, and it does not look as though I shall ever lose it now. Old age naturally restricts a man, his strength is gradually exhausted, but by way of compensation I now have not only more stored-up experience but a greater inner freedom.

Writing these memoirs has not been easy. No matter how much I may have written about the soarings of science or the struggle for peace, I was keenly aware that I was nevertheless making a personal confession in public. What has helped me was the knowledge that by writing about departed friends and about myself, by invoking names of people who have been dear to me, I was fighting off oblivion, the void, non-existence, which, according to Joliot, human nature abhors.

I knew when I started that this work would be criticized; that there would be those who would say I had kept silent about too many things, and those who would think I had said too much. In the foreword I wrote in 1963 to the second volume of these memoirs for its publication in book form in the Soviet Union, I said: 'This book, *Men, Years – Life*, has provoked many discussions and critical remarks. I should like to stress once again that the book is the story of my life, of the searchings, errors and discoveries of one man. It is therefore extremely subjective and I have never claimed to be writing a history of the epoch'.

It is not so much my book as my life that has been and will be criticized. But I cannot begin my life anew. I have admitted my many mistakes and instances of thoughtlessness too often to assume the role of an aged mentor. I myself, for that matter, would gladly listen to the wise men capable of answering the questions that still harass me. I set out to tell the story of the years I have lived and the people I have known; yet, possibly, some of my readers may be helped by thinking over and understanding certain things about which I have written.

Today I have too many desires and not enough strength. I shall end with a confession: I hate indifference, curtained windows, harshness and the cruelty of isolation. While I was writing about friends who are no more, I sometimes stopped working, went up to the window and stood there as one stands at meetings in respectful silence for the dead; I did not look at the green leaves or at the snowdrifts, I saw only the face dear to me. Many passages in these memoirs have been dictated by love. I love life; I do not repent, I do not regret what I have lived through and what I have experienced; what I regret is that there is so much that I have not done, not written; that

I have not grieved and not loved enough. But that is how life goes; the audience is already hurrying to the exits while on the stage the hero is still singing: 'Tomorrow it will be I . . .'[1] And what *will* be tomorrow? Another play, a different set of characters.

[1] From *The Queen of Spades.*

1962–64. Revised 1965

ILYA EHRENBURG

Babi Yar

No monument stands over Babi Yar.
A drop sheer as a crude gravestone.
I am afraid.
                    Today I am as old in years
as all the Jewish people.
Now I seem to be
                    a Jew.
Here I plod through ancient Egypt.
Here I perish crucified, on the cross,
and to this day I bear the scars of nails.
I seem to be
                    Dreyfus.
The Philistine
                    is both informer and judge.
I am behind bars.
                    Beset on every side.
Hounded,
          spat on,
                    slandered.
Squealing, dainty ladies in flounced
Brussels lace
stick their parasols into my face.
I seem to be then
                    a young boy in Byelostok.
Blood runs, spilling over the floors.
The bar-room rabble-rousers
give off a stench of vodka and onion.
A boot kicks me aside, helpless.
In vain I plead with these pogrom bullies.

While they jeer and shout,
                    'Beat the Yids. Save Russia!'
some grain-marketeer beats up my mother.
O my Russian people!
                    I know
                              you
are international to the core.
But those with unclean hands
have often made a jingle of your
purest name.
I know the goodness of my land.
How vile these anti-Semites –
                         without a qualm
they pompously called themselves
'The Union of the Russian People'!
I seem to be
              Anne Frank
transparent
              as a branch in April.
And I love
              And have no need of phrases.
My need
         is that we gaze into each other.
How little we can see
                    or smell!
We are denied the leaves,
                    we are denied the sky.
Yet we can do so much –
                    tenderly
embrace each other in a dark room.
They're coming here?
         Be not afraid. Those are the booming
sounds of spring:
                    spring is coming here.

Come then to me.
               Quick, give me your lips.
Are they smashing down the door?
                    No, it's the ice breaking . . .
The wild grasses rustle over Babi Yar.
The trees look ominous,
                         like judges.
Here all things scream silently,
                    and, baring my head,
slowly I feel myself
                    turning gray.
And I myself
               am one massive, soundless scream
above the thousand thousand buried here.
I am
       each old man
                    here shot dead.
I am
       every child
                    here shot dead.
Nothing in me
               shall ever forget!
The 'Internationale', let it
                         thunder
when the last anti-Semite on earth
is buried forever.
In my blood there is no Jewish blood.
In their callous rage, all anti-Semites
must hate me now as a Jew.
For that reason
               I am a true Russian!

                         YEVGENY YEVTUSENKO

Acknowledgements

WHERE authors' names have been supplied, acknowledgement is made to the following sources: 'Letter to a Non-Commissioned Officer' by Leo Tolstoy, from *The Pacifist Conscience* by Peter Mayer, published by Rupert Hart-Davis Ltd: 'No Justification' by Z. N. Hippius, 'To be famous is unbecoming' by Boris Pasternak, 'Sweet Clover' by I. A. Bunin and 'Prayer' by Anna Akhmatova, are all from *Modern Russian Poetry*, edited and with an introduction by Vladimir Markov and Merrill Sparks, published by MacGibbon & Kee Ltd. A number of pieces have not previously appeared in translation, and among these are: 'The Death of Dolgushov' by Isaac Babel, 'How They Wrote Robinson Crusoe' by I'lf and Petrov, both to appear in a new volume of modern Russian short stories, to be published by MacGibbon & Kee Ltd. Ilya Ehrenburg's contribution is taken from *Post-War Years*, published by MacGibbon & Kee Ltd. In a number of cases the authors' names have been withheld and consequently the source is not given.